Chapter Tutorials for St... Parents, Mentors, and Peers

(HOLT)

Call to Freedom
Beginnings to 1877

HOLT, RINEHART AND WINSTON
A Harcourt Education Company

Austin · New York · Orlando · Atlanta · San Francisco · Boston · Dallas · Toronto · London

Cover: Christie's Images

Printed in the United States of America

ISBN 0-03-065226-X

3 4 5 6 7 8 9 085 04 03

Contents

Each chapter of *Call to Freedom: Beginnings to 1877* has a corresponding chapter tutorial to provide a tool for other individuals, besides the teacher, who may be taking part in helping students learn. The tutorials provide parents, mentors, and peers the ability to work with students to cover key chapter material for future assessment.

CHAPTER 1

Chapter Tutorial

The World Before the Opening of the Atlantic

IDENTIFYING TERMS Choose the term or name that correctly matches each definition.

_____ **1.** groups that share a common culture

_____ **2.** developed by local rulers to defend against invasions

_____ **3.** study of the unwritten past

_____ **4.** trade route stretching from the Black Sea to China

_____ **5.** unique political confederation

a. archaeology

b. societies

c. Iroquois League

d. feudalism

e. Silk Road

UNDERSTANDING MAIN IDEAS

1. How did Paleo-Indians adapt to the changing environment at the end of the Ice Age?

_____

_____

2. What were some important aspects of Inca society?

_____

_____

3. How did cultures vary within the Great Plains region?

_____

_____

4. Where did the Vikings establish colonies?

_____

_____

5. How did trade affect city-states in Africa?

_____

_____

REVIEWING THEMES

1. Culture What similarities did Native Americans living in the same region share?

_____

_____

2. Geography How did Native Americans' houses reflect adjustment to their environment?

_____

_____

3. Global Relations How did civilizations in Africa, Asia, and the Muslim Empire benefit from trade?

_____

_____

THINKING CRITICALLY

1. Identifying Cause and Effect How did developments in farming encourage the growth of towns in Europe during the Middle Ages?

_____

_____

2. Analyzing Information Why did the system of feudalism develop in Europe during the Middle Ages?

_____

_____

WRITING ABOUT HISTORY

Informing Imagine that you are a monk or nun living during the Middle Ages. Write a letter to a relative describing your daily activities.

_____

_____

_____

_____

The World Before the Opening of the Atlantic

IDENTIFYING TERMS Choose the term or name that correctly matches each definition.

_b (p. 6)_ **1.** groups that share a common culture

_d (p. 19)_ **2.** developed by local rulers to defend against invasions

_a (p. 5)_ **3.** study of the unwritten past

_e (p. 25)_ **4.** trade route stretching from the Black Sea to China

_c (p. 16)_ **5.** unique political confederation

a. archaeology

b. societies

c. Iroquois League

d. feudalism

e. Silk Road

UNDERSTANDING MAIN IDEAS

1. How did Paleo-Indians adapt to the changing environment at the end of the Ice Age?

Paleo-Indians adapted to the environmental changes by hunting smaller mammals and birds, and by relying more on seeds, berries, nuts, and edible leaves and roots.

2. What were some important aspects of Inca society?

The Inca controlled a vast empire with a large network of roads. In the capital the Inca built large palaces with bathrooms and running water. Inca subjects remained in their own villages and kept their local customs. Families worked together dig canals and grow crops that fed the empire.

3. How did cultures vary within the Great Plains region?

Peoples in the northern and central Plains grew crops. The Pawnee had a matrilineal society. On the southern plains, people hunted buffalo and gathered other food. On the eastern and western borders of the Plains, hunters sometimes killed huge numbers of buffalo by chasing the animals over steep cliffs.

4. Where did the Vikings establish colonies?

They established colonies in Iceland, Greenland, and briefly in North America.

5. How did trade affect city-states in Africa?

City-states in Africa grew wealthy from trade and developed unique cultures by mixing outside influences such as Islam with native African ideas.

REVIEWING THEMES

1. Culture What similarities did Native Americans living in the same region share?

Native Americans living in the same region had similar environments, housing, language, and methods of obtaining food.

2. Geography How did Native Americans' houses reflect adjustment to their environment?

The Anasazi used natural geographic features for protection when they built multi-story mesa and cliff dwellings. The Aleut and Inuit built underground houses and igloos using local materials to protect themselves from very cold conditions. In the East, Native Americans used local materials to build multi-family lodges, wigwams, longhouses.

3. Global Relations How did civilizations in Africa, Asia, and the Muslim Empire benefit from trade?

Africa—trade built wealthy empires and created unique cultures that incorporated the religion of Islam; Asia—trade brought wealth and knowledge of other cultures; Muslim Empire—traders helped spread Islam and allowed people to exchange new ideas.

THINKING CRITICALLY

1. Identifying Cause and Effect How did developments in farming encourage the growth of towns in Europe during the Middle Ages?

Changes in farming led to increased food production so that the farms could support larger populations. Larger populations and the demand for trade helped towns to grow.

2. Analyzing Information Why did the system of feudalism develop in Europe during the Middle Ages?

Nobles needed armed knights to defend their manors from attack. Peasants farmed a lord's land or performed other services in return for the lord's protection.

WRITING ABOUT HISTORY

Informing Imagine that you are a monk or nun living during the Middle Ages. Write a letter to a relative describing your daily activities.

Letters should mention the religious and scholarly purpose of monasteries and convents. Letters about monks should mention giving up personal possessions, but running large estates. Letters about convents should mention the tasks women might do there as well as the opportunities women could find.

Name _____ Class _____ Date _____

Chapter Tutorial

The Age of Exploration

IDENTIFYING TERMS Choose the term or name that correctly matches each definition.

_____ **1.** to sail completely around something

_____ **2.** the transfer of plants, animals, and disease between the Old World and the New World

_____ **3.** economic control of a product or service

_____ **4.** royal governor

_____ **5.** small but sturdy ship

a. monopoly

b. caravel

c. viceroy

d. circumnavigate

e. Columbian Exchange

UNDERSTANDING MAIN IDEAS

1. How did the Commercial Revolution change Europe's economy?

_____

_____

2. What was unusual about the route Columbus planned to take to Asia?

_____

_____

3. What route did Vasco da Gama take to reach India?

_____

_____

4. Why was the importance of Balboa's discovery of the South Sea?

_____

_____

5. Why did some explorers search for a Northwest Passage?

_____

_____

Chapter 2 Tutorial, continued

REVIEWING THEMES

1. Global Relations Describe the Columbian Exchange and its effects on Europeans and American Indians.

_____

_____

2. Economics Explain how the expansion of trade affected the economic development of Spain and Portugal.

_____

_____

3. Science, Technology & Society How did technology encourage voyages of exploration?

_____

_____

THINKING CRITICALLY

1. Evaluating How did slavery affect African communities?

_____

_____

2. Synthesizing How did Portugal take the lead in the race for a sea route to Asia?

_____

_____

WRITING ABOUT HISTORY

Describing Imagine that you are a Taino native who has just encountered Columbus in 1492. Describe your impressions of the Europeans and discuss how you expect American Indians and Europeans to help each other.

_____

_____

_____

_____

IDENTIFYING TERMS Choose the term or name that correctly matches each definition.

d (p. 49) **1.** to sail completely around something

e (p. 51) **2.** the transfer of plants, animals, and disease between the Old World and the New World

a (p. 35) **3.** economic control of a product or service

c (p. 39) **4.** royal governor

b (p. 36) **5.** small but sturdy ship

a. monopoly

b. caravel

c. viceroy

d. circumnavigate

e. Columbian Exchange

UNDERSTANDING MAIN IDEAS

1. How did the Commercial Revolution change Europe's economy?

The Commercial Revolution changed the way many merchants conducted business. Merchants became more aggressive about earning money and they established banks as a way to get capital and to make more money.

2. What was unusual about the route Columbus planned to take to Asia?

Columbus planned to reach Asia by sailing west across the Atlantic Ocean, rather than by sailing around Africa as the Portuguese were attempting.

3. What route did Vasco da Gama take to reach India?

Vasco da Gama sailed from Portugal around Africa's Cape of Good Hope to reach India.

4. Why was the importance of Balboa's discovery of the South Sea?

It gave Spain new hope of finding a western sea route to Asia.

5. Why did some explorers search for a Northwest Passage?

They wanted to find a path around or through North America that would allow ships to sail from the Atlantic to the Pacific.

REVIEWING THEMES

1. Global Relations Describe the Columbian Exchange and its effects on Europeans and American Indians.

It was a transfer of plants, animals, and diseases between the "Old World" of Europe and the "New World" of the Americas. Europeans incorporated new food items, such as potatoes and tomatoes, into their diet. They brought horses, cattle, and pigs to America. American Indians used these animals for transportation and as food. Europeans also brought wheat and barley, as well as diseases for which American Indians did not have immunity. Large numbers of American Indians died from these diseases.

2. Economics Explain how the expansion of trade affected the economic development of Spain and Portugal.

Spanish and Portuguese traders made greater profits because they no longer dealt with third parties such as Muslim traders. Spain and Portugal also gained great influence in European affairs.

3. Science, Technology & Society How did technology encourage voyages of exploration?

During the Renaissance, sailors invented the magnetic compass and the astrolabe. Both inventions helped sailors navigate in the open sea without any landmarks to guide them.

THINKING CRITICALLY

1. Evaluating How did slavery affect African communities?

It led to more warfare among the kingdoms of West Africa and broke up many families.

2. Synthesizing How did Portugal take the lead in the race for a sea route to Asia?

Prince Henry gathered together the finest mapmakers, sailors, and shipbuilders in Sagres; he also helped improve navigational instruments such as the compass and paid for expeditions.

WRITING ABOUT HISTORY

Describing Imagine that you are a Taino native who has just encountered Columbus in 1492. Describe your impressions of the Europeans and discuss how you expect American Indians and Europeans to help each other.

Essays should be from the perspective of a Taino native. Essays should include a physical description of the Europeans and of their ships, and a description of the Europeans' language. Essays should include how the Tainos helped the Europeans and gave them goods and how the Europeans wanted only to find gold.

Name _____ Class _____ Date _____

 **CHAPTER 3**   Chapter Tutorial

New Empires in the Americas

IDENTIFYING TERMS Choose the term or name that correctly matches each definition.

_____ **1.** Spanish soldiers who led military expeditions in the Americas

_____ **2.** settlements established to convert American Indians to Catholicism

_____ **3.** outer reaches of New Spain where few settlers lived

_____ **4.** large farms that grew just one kind of crop

_____ **5.** reformers who criticized the Catholic Church

a. missions

b. Protestants

c. conquistadores

d. plantations

e. borderlands

UNDERSTANDING MAIN IDEAS

1. What role did Hernán Cortés play in the fall of the Aztec Empire?

_____

_____

2. Describe the *encomienda* system of New Spain.

_____

_____

3. Why did many Europeans leave the Catholic Church to become Protestants?

_____

_____

4. What difficulties did settlers in the Roanoke colonies face?

_____

_____

REVIEWING THEMES

1. Global Relations How did the conquistadores defeat large native populations in the Americas?

_____

_____

2. Geography Why were France, Sweden, and the Netherlands, interested in establishing colonies in North America?

_____

_____

3. Economics How did Spain's economy benefit from the colonies?

_____

_____

THINKING CRITICALLY

1. Analyzing Why did Bartolomé de Las Casas oppose the encomienda system?

_____

_____

2. Assessing Consequences How was Spain affected by the English defeat of the Spanish Armada?

_____

_____

WRITING ABOUT HISTORY

Persuading Imagine that you are Queen Elizabeth I. Deliver a speech to your subjects in an effort to maintain peace between Protestants and Catholics.

_____

_____

_____

_____

IDENTIFYING TERMS Choose the term or name that correctly matches each definition.

<u>c (p. 66)</u> **1.** Spanish soldiers who led military expeditions in the Americas

<u>a (p. 73)</u> **2.** settlements established to convert American Indians to Catholicism

<u>e (p. 75)</u> **3.** outer reaches of New Spain where few settlers lived

<u>d (p. 74)</u> **4.** large farms that grew just one kind of crop

<u>b (p. 78)</u> **5.** reformers who criticized the Catholic Church

a. missions

b. Protestants

c. conquistadores

d. plantations

e. borderlands

UNDERSTANDING MAIN IDEAS

1. What role did Hernán Cortés play in the fall of the Aztec Empire?

Cortés took the Aztec leader Moctezuma prisoner, and then fought the Aztecs for several months. The Spanish also brought diseases with them that caused hundreds of thousands of deaths and quickened the fall of the Aztec Empire.

2. Describe the *encomienda* system of New Spain.

Spanish settlers were given the right to tax local American Indians or force them to work. In exchange, these settlers were supposed to convert local Indians to Christianity, as well as protect and teach them.

3. Why did many Europeans leave the Catholic Church to become Protestants?

They left the Catholic Church because they were protesting the Church's practices. Protestants believed that the Bible intended for religion to be simple. They thought the Catholic Church had too many rules and they objected to the great power held by the pope.

4. What difficulties did settlers in the Roanoke colonies face?

The settlers fought with local American Indians and had trouble finding and growing food.

REVIEWING THEMES

1. Global Relations How did the conquistadores defeat large native populations in the Americas?

The conquistadores used superior weapons, horses, and American Indian allies. Disease also greatly weakened native populations.

2. Geography Why were France, Sweden, and the Netherlands, interested in establishing colonies in North America?

France, Sweden, and the Netherlands wanted to trade with American Indians for valuable furs and to farm good land.

3. Economics How did Spain's economy benefit from the colonies?

Spain gained enormous wealth from its colonies.

THINKING CRITICALLY

1. Analyzing Why did Bartolomé de Las Casas oppose the encomienda system?

Las Casas believed the encomienda system violated American Indians' rights by forcing them to work under extremely harsh conditions.

2. Assessing Consequences How was Spain affected by the English defeat of the Spanish Armada?

The defeat of the Armada ended King Philip's plan to conquer England and shocked Spain. It also weakened the Spanish navy so that it could no longer protect its empire in the Americas. Countries such as England, France, and the Netherlands began challenging Spanish power abroad.

WRITING ABOUT HISTORY

Persuading Imagine that you are Queen Elizabeth I. Deliver a speech to your subjects in an effort to maintain peace between Protestants and Catholics.

Speeches should be formal in style and address all subjects. Speeches should mention the importance of peace between Protestants and Catholics as a way to protect England from King Philip of Spain. Speeches should emphasize similarities between the Catholic Church and the Anglican Church.

CHAPTER 4

Chapter Tutorial
The English Colonies

IDENTIFYING TERMS Choose the term or name that correctly matches each definition.

_____ **1.** people who worked up to seven years to repay ship fare

_____ **2.** religious group

_____ **3.** people who came to a new country after leaving the land of their birth

_____ **4.** helped Pilgrims establish relations with Massasoit

_____ **5.** people who disagree with official opinions

a. sect

b. dissenters

c. Squanto

d. indentured servants

e. immigrants

UNDERSTANDING MAIN IDEAS

1. What caused the frequent conflicts between the Jamestown colonists and the Powhatan?

_____

_____

2. Why did Nathaniel Bacon and his followers rebel and burn Jamestown?

_____

_____

3. Why did the Pilgrims leave the Netherlands to come to America?

_____

_____

4. How was the Massachusetts Bay Colony organized?

_____

_____

5. Who were the settlers in Oglethorpe's colony of Georgia?

_____

_____

Chapter 4 Tutorial, continued

REVIEWING THEMES

1. Geography How did the weather in Massachusetts and South Carolina lead colonists to develop different ways of making a living?

_____

_____

2. Economics How did plantation owners deal with the labor shortage in Virginia?

_____

_____

3. Culture Why did the Great Migration occur?

_____

_____

THINKING CRITICALLY

1. Drawing Inferences and Conclusions What might have attracted women to the Quaker faith?

_____

_____

2. Comparing What role did religion play in the colonies of Rhode Island and Maryland?

_____

_____

WRITING ABOUT HISTORY

Informing Imagine that you were present at the trial of Anne Hutchinson. Write an article for a Massachusetts newspaper describing the trial.

_____

_____

_____

_____

IDENTIFYING TERMS Choose the term or name that correctly matches each definition.

_d (p. 96)_ **1.** people who worked up to seven years to repay ship fare

_a (p. 98)_ **2.** religious group

_e (p. 99)_ **3.** people who came to a new country after leaving the land of their birth

_c (p. 101)_ **4.** helped Pilgrims establish relations with Massasoit

_b (p. 103)_ **5.** people who disagree with official opinions

a. sect

b. dissenters

c. Squanto

d. indentured servants

e. immigrants

UNDERSTANDING MAIN IDEAS

1. What caused the frequent conflicts between the Jamestown colonists and the Powhatan?

At first there were conflicts because the colonists took food from the Powhatan by force. Later, when the colonists were no longer dependent on the American Indians for food, the colonists hoped to take over Powhatan lands.

2. Why did Nathaniel Bacon and his followers rebel and burn Jamestown?

These colonists were protesting the high taxes and the lack of available farmland.

3. Why did the Pilgrims leave the Netherlands to come to America?

They felt their children were learning Dutch language and culture rather than English traditions.

4. How was the Massachusetts Bay Colony organized?

The company charter created a General Court to run the colony. Each town sent two or three delegates to the Court. Eventually the Court elected the colony's governor and his assistants. In 1644, the Court became a two-house legislature. Religion and politics were closely linked and male church members were the only colonists who could vote. To become full members in the church, colonists had to pass a public test to prove that their faith was strong.

5. Who were the settlers in Oglethorpe's colony of Georgia?

Georgia was founded as a place for poor people and people who had been jailed for debt.

REVIEWING THEMES

1. Geography How did the weather in Massachusetts and South Carolina lead colonists to develop different ways of making a living?

The Massachusetts region had a healthy climate so few colonists died from sickness and this helped the colony succeed. In Virginia, marshes filled with disease-carrying mosquitoes and the poor quality of water led to the deaths of many colonists. This caused serious labor shortages and made success very difficult.

2. Economics How did plantation owners deal with the labor shortage in Virginia?

They used a system in which indentured servants agreed to work for a plantation owner from four to seven years in exchange for their ship fare to Virginia.

3. Culture Why did the Great Migration occur?

The Great Migration occurred because there was an economic downturn in England which was made worse when King Charles I raised taxes. In addition, the Church of England began to harass dissenters and attack those who opposed the official church. These factors led thousands of people to leave England.

THINKING CRITICALLY

1. Drawing Inferences and Conclusions What might have attracted women to the Quaker faith?

Women might have been attracted to the Quaker faith because Quakers believed that men and women were equal before God.

2. Comparing What role did religion play in the colonies of Rhode Island and Maryland?

Rhode Island was founded by people who disagreed with the Puritans' leadership in Massachusetts. Led by Roger Williams, these dissenters believed the church should be separated from politics and supported religious tolerance. Rhode Island accepted dissidents such as Anne Hutchinson and her followers who were persecuted for their beliefs in Massachusetts. Maryland was founded by English Catholics who came to America to escape religious persecution. Maryland passed one of the first laws supporting religious tolerance in the English colonies.

WRITING ABOUT HISTORY

Informing Imagine that you were present at the trial of Anne Hutchinson. Write an article for a Massachusetts newspaper describing the trial.

Articles should explain Hutchinson's beliefs, why the Puritans were trying her, and explain the verdict in the trial.

CHAPTER 5

Chapter Tutorial

Life in the English Colonies

IDENTIFYING TERMS Choose the term or name that correctly matches each definition.

_____ **1.** group that set policy for the British colonies

_____ **2.** goods bought from other countries

_____ **3.** boys sent to craftsmen to learn a trade

_____ **4.** public religious gatherings to hear sermons and declare faith

_____ **5.** also called the Age of Reason

a. imports

b. revivals

c. Enlightenment

d. Privy Council

e. apprentices

UNDERSTANDING MAIN IDEAS

1. How did England organize the government of the thirteen colonies?

_____

_____

2. Compare the economies of the New England, middle, and southern colonies.

_____

_____

3. What were the economic roles of women in the colonies?

_____

_____

4. Why did some people believe that American colonists were in need of a "great awakening"?

_____

_____

5. Who were the most influential writers of the colonial period, and what did they write?

_____

_____

Chapter 5 Tutorial, continued

REVIEWING THEMES

1. Economics How did the Navigation Acts restrict colonial trade?

_____

_____

2. Geography How did the climate influence the types of crops grown in southern colonies?

_____

_____

3. Science, Technology & Society What scientific advances were made by colonial Americans?

_____

_____

THINKING CRITICALLY

1. Making Generalizations What was the relationship between religion and education in the colonies?

_____

_____

2. Drawing Conclusions Why might the Great Awakening have inspired a movement for greater democracy?

_____

_____

WRITING ABOUT HISTORY

Describing Imagine that you are a craftsman living in New England. Create a help wanted ad for an apprentice. Remember to include information about your craft, as well as job requirements. Keep in mind that a new apprentice will have little or no experience before hiring.

_____

_____

_____

_____

IDENTIFYING TERMS Choose the term or name that correctly matches each definition.

_d (p. 120)_ **1.** group that set policy for the British colonies

_a (p. 126)_ **2.** goods bought from other countries

_e (p. 133)_ **3.** boys sent to craftsmen to learn a trade

_b (p. 136)_ **4.** public religious gatherings to hear sermons and declare faith

_c (p. 141)_ **5.** also called the Age of Reason

a. imports

b. revivals

c. Enlightenment

d. Privy Council

e. apprentices

UNDERSTANDING MAIN IDEAS

1. How did England organize the government of the thirteen colonies?

The Privy Council in England set policy for the colonies but it allowed the colonies to govern themselves. Each colony had a governor, who usually were assisted by an advisory council. Some colonies had a body of elected representatives that was modeled on the English Parliament.

2. Compare the economies of the New England, middle, and southern colonies.

The southern colonies used slave labor to produce agricultural products, and they also exported materials for shipbuilding. New England's largest industries were fishing and shipbuilding. These colonies depended on skilled craftspeople to produce goods. The middle colonies combined aspects of the New England and southern colonies. They had both trade and agriculture and relied on indentured servants for labor.

3. What were the economic roles of women in the colonies?

Some women became involved in the colonial economy by running businesses and farms and practicing medicine. However, most women worked in the home, contributing to the economy by providing goods and services to the family or selling goods outside the home.

4. Why did some people believe that American colonists were in need of a "great awakening"?

Some feared that the colonists' dedication to their religion was declining and that the religious commitment of previous generations had been lost.

5. Who were the most influential writers of the colonial period, and what did they write?

Ministers such as John Cotton, Jonathan Edwards, and Cotton Mather wrote dramatic and influential sermons. Anne Bradstreet wrote about her family and her faith. Phillis Wheatley wrote poetry that used religious language and imagery.

REVIEWING THEMES

1. Economics How did the Navigation Acts restrict colonial trade?

The Acts required the colonies to do most of their trading with England and set duties on some trade products.

2. Geography How did the climate influence the types of crops grown in southern colonies?

Warm climate and long growing seasons led the southern colonies to rely on cash crops that could be grown and exported for profit.

3. Science, Technology & Society What scientific advances were made by colonial Americans?

David Rittenhouse developed mathematical and astronomical instruments, while Benjamin Banneker accurately predicted an eclipse. Benjamin Franklin proved that lightning was a form of electricity and he identified electricity's positive and negative charges. He also invented the lightning rod, Franklin stove, and bifocals.

THINKING CRITICALLY

1. Making Generalizations What was the relationship between religion and education in the colonies?

In New England, religious beliefs encouraged people to read the Bible and value educated ministers. Thus, throughout New England, communities paid for elementary schools. In the southern and middle colonies children were taught by their parents or tutors rather than in religious communities.

2. Drawing Conclusions Why might the Great Awakening have inspired a movement for greater democracy?

The Great Awakening carried a message of the spiritual equality of all people. This may have led some colonists to demand more political equality. In addition, revivals provided places for the colonists to discuss politics and increased communication among people in different colonies.

WRITING ABOUT HISTORY

Describing Imagine that you are a craftsman living in New England. Create a help wanted ad for an apprentice. Remember to include information about your craft, as well as job requirements. Keep in mind that a new apprentice will have little or no experience before hiring.

The advertisements should mention the types of crafts that were needed in New England and should explain the terms of apprenticeship.

CHAPTER **6**

Chapter Tutorial

Conflicts in the Colonies

IDENTIFYING TERMS Choose the term or name that correctly matches each definition.

_____ **1.** group of civilians serving as soldiers

_____ **2.** Wampanoag chief who opposed further colonial expansion

_____ **3.** method of protest in which people refuse to buy goods

_____ **4.** information giving only one side of an argument

_____ **5.** law that allowed the British East India Tea Company to sell tea directly to the colonists

a. Metacomet

b. propaganda

c. militia

d. Tea Act

e. boycott

UNDERSTANDING MAIN IDEAS

1. What caused the frequent conflicts between English and French colonists?

_____

_____

2. Identify the factors that led to Pontiac's Rebellion.

_____

_____

3. Why did the British create new taxes for the colonists?

_____

_____

4. How did the Boston Massacre show the British that the colonists were willing to defy British authority?

_____

_____

Chapter 6 Tutorial, continued

REVIEWING THEMES

1. Global Relations How did conflicts between Britain and France affect British colonists in America?

_____

_____

2. Geography Describe the relationship between American Indians and English colonists.

_____

_____

3. Economics What were the main reasons that British colonists objected to the taxes imposed by Parliament in the late 1760s and early 1770s?

_____

_____

THINKING CRITICALLY

1. Making Predictions How do you think American Indians would have reacted if the British had been interested in sharing land rights?

_____

_____

2. Supporting a Point of View Do you think that it was fair that the British expected American colonists to pay taxes to England? Explain why or why not.

_____

_____

WRITING ABOUT HISTORY

Informing Imagine that you are a pioneer living in a British fort on the North American frontier. Write a poem in support of the Proclamation of 1763.

_____

_____

_____

_____

Conflicts in the Colonies

IDENTIFYING TERMS Choose the term or name that correctly matches each definition.

c (p. 158) **1.** group of civilians serving as soldiers

a (p. 158) **2.** Wampanoag chief who opposed further colonial expansion

e (p. 169) **3.** method of protest in which people refuse to buy goods

b (p. 172) **4.** information giving only one side of an argument

d (p. 173) **5.** law that allowed the British East India Tea Company to sell tea directly to the colonists

a. Metacomet

b. propaganda

c. militia

d. Tea Act

e. boycott

UNDERSTANDING MAIN IDEAS

1. What caused the frequent conflicts between English and French colonists?

Conflicts between English and French colonists were caused by both wanting control of Europe and North America.

2. Identify the factors that led to Pontiac's Rebellion.

After the French and Indian War, Britain gained control of the Ohio River valley. American Indian peoples living there opposed British settlement. To protest, groups in the area joined together and attempted to drive out white settlers.

3. Why did the British create new taxes for the colonists?

The British raised taxes in the colonies because they needed to pay off the expense of the wars fought to protect the colonies.

4. How did the Boston Massacre show the British that the colonists were willing to defy British authority?

The crowd that gathered around the British soldiers showed that they did not respect British authority by throwing snowballs and shouting insults at the troops. In addition, the propaganda spread about the incident later showed the colonists' willingness to spread anti-British ideas.

REVIEWING THEMES

1. Global Relations How did conflicts between Britain and France affect British colonists in America?

These international conflicts led to a series of wars fought in the colonies over territories that both countries wanted. Great Britain's victory in the French and Indian War added a great deal of territory to Britain's holdings in North America. However, it also left the British with a large war debt that British leaders hoped that the colonists would help pay. Disputes over these taxes led the colonists to begin considering revolution.

2. Geography Describe the relationship between American Indians and English colonists.

The relationship between American Indians and English colonists was uneasy. On the one hand, both groups depended on each other for trade. On the other hand, the colonists often wanted to take over American Indian lands. Indians hoping to prevent colonists from taking away their homes would often form alliances among themselves to drive out the English colonists.

3. Economics What were the main reasons that British colonists objected to the taxes imposed by Parliament in the late 1760s and early 1770s?

Colonists objected to these taxes because they felt they were unfair and bad for business. Having been very independent until that time, colonists felt that Britain did not have the right to tax the colonies because the colonies did not consent to the taxes.

THINKING CRITICALLY

1. Making Predictions How do you think American Indians would have reacted if the British had been interested in sharing land rights?

Students may say that the American Indians might have been more peaceful and that much conflict could have been avoided had the colonists been willing to share. Other students, however, might say that the ways the colonists and the American Indians' lives were so different that conflict was inevitable. In addition, some might suggest that the Indians had no reason to agree to share land that was already theirs.

2. Supporting a Point of View Do you think that it was fair that the British expected American colonists to pay taxes to England? Explain why or why not.

Students might say that because the colonists were protected and they gained new territories to move into that they should have helped pay. Others might argue that the war was primarily a European conflict and that the colonists had little to do with it. In addition, students might mention that Parliament ought to have allowed the colonies representation before taxing them.

WRITING ABOUT HISTORY

Informing Imagine that you are a pioneer living in a British fort on the North American frontier. Write a poem in support of the Proclamation of 1763.

Poems should consider the American Indian unrest that the colonists were causing by moving into these lands and the expense of continued fighting.

Chapter Tutorial

The American Revolution

IDENTIFYING TERMS Choose the term or name that correctly matches each definition.

_____ **1.** soldiers surrounding a city or fort

_____ **2.** wrote a popular pamphlet called *Common Sense*

_____ **3.** swift, hit-and-run attacks

_____ **4.** colonists who fought for independence

_____ **5.** colonists who sided with Britain

a. guerilla warfare

b. siege

c. Thomas Paine

d. Patriots

e. Loyalists

UNDERSTANDING MAIN IDEAS

1. How did *Common Sense* affect the American colonists' attitude toward Britain?

_____

_____

2. Did the Declaration of Independence address the rights of all colonists? Explain.

_____

_____

3. What tactic did the Patriots use to defeat the British at Trenton and Princeton?

_____

_____

4. How did the victory at Saratoga affect the Patriots?

_____

_____

Chapter 7 Tutorial, continued

REVIEWING THEMES

1. Citizenship Why did the colonists revolt against their ruling government?

_____

_____

2. Constitutional heritage How does the Declaration of Independence reflect Enlightenment beliefs?

_____

_____

3. Global Relations Why were France and Spain interested in supporting the Patriots' revolution?

_____

_____

THINKING CRITICALLY

1. Contrasting What were the main differences between the First and Second Continental Congresses?

_____

_____

2. Drawing Conclusions Why did some American Indians support the British in the war?

_____

_____

WRITING ABOUT HISTORY

Expressing Imagine that you are a Patriot guerrilla fighter who has just narrowly escaped after an attack on a British camp. Write a paragraph in your journal about why you chose this role in the Revolution and what it is like.

_____

_____

_____

_____

IDENTIFYING TERMS Choose the term or name that correctly matches each definition.

b (p. 187) **1.** situation in which soldiers surround a city or fort

a. guerilla warfare

c (p. 190) **2.** wrote a popular pamphlet called *Common Sense*

b. siege

a (p. 211) **3.** swift, hit-and-run attacks

c. Thomas Paine

d (p. 192) **4.** colonists who fought for independence

d. Patriots

e (p. 192) **5.** colonists who sided with Britain

e. Loyalists

UNDERSTANDING MAIN IDEAS

1. How did *Common Sense* affect the American colonists' attitude toward Britain?

The idea of independence gained more and more supporters.

2. Did the Declaration of Independence address the rights of all colonists? Explain.

The Declaration did not address the rights of women or of slaves.

3. What tactic did the Patriots use to defeat the British at Trenton and Princeton?

The Patriots used surprise attacks.

4. How did the victory at Saratoga affect the Patriots?

Saratoga marked the Patriots' greatest victory up to that point and boosted foreign countries' support for the Patriots.

REVIEWING THEMES

1. Citizenship Why did the colonists revolt against their ruling government?

The colonists revolted because they believed Great Britain was violating their rights. The colonists attacked the king for passing unfair laws, interfering with colonial self-government, and imposing taxes without the colonists' consent.

2. Constitutional heritage How does the Declaration of Independence reflect Enlightenment beliefs?

Unalienable rights, including "life, liberty, and the pursuit of happiness" reflect the Enlightenment writings of John Locke.

3. Global Relations Why were France and Spain interested in supporting the Patriots' revolution?

France and Spain were bitter, longtime enemies of Britain.

THINKING CRITICALLY

1. Contrasting What were the main differences between the First and Second Continental Congresses?

The First Congress decided to continue to boycott British goods and to warn their militias to be prepared in case of violence. It also sent a list of resolutions to King George III. The Second Congress created the Continental Army to defend the colonies and chose George Washington to command the army. The delegates also signed the Olive Branch Petition in a last attempt to keep peace.

2. Drawing Conclusions Why did some American Indians support the British in the war?

American Indians may have supported the British because the Indians were already allies with the British and because the British had a powerful military with trained professionals. Britain also had the most powerful navy in the world.

WRITING ABOUT HISTORY

Expressing Imagine that you are a Patriot guerrilla fighter who has just narrowly escaped after an attack on a British camp. Write a paragraph in your journal about why you chose this role in the Revolution and what it is like.

Paragraphs should be in the voice of a guerrilla fighter. Paragraphs should discuss hit-and-run attacks and where and why they occurred. Reasons for choosing the role of a guerrilla fighter might include location or style of fighting.

CHAPTER 8

Forming a Government

IDENTIFYING TERMS Choose the term or name that correctly matches each definition.

_____ **1.** set of laws that determine the duties of the government

_____ **2.** official approval

_____ **3.** low economic activity and high unemployment

_____ **4.** distribution of power between states and the central government

_____ **5.** series of essays that supported the Constitution

a. ratification

b. federalism

c. constitution

d. *Federalist Papers*

e. depression

UNDERSTANDING MAIN IDEAS

1. On which English laws did Americans base their political ideas for government?

_____

_____

2. How could new states be created under the Northwest Ordinance?

_____

_____

3. How did the Articles of Confederation interfere with interstate commerce?

_____

_____

4. How did the writers of the Constitution address the concerns of Antifederalists?

_____

_____

Chapter 8 Tutorial, *continued*

REVIEWING THEMES

1. Global Relations How did England and Spain take advantage of the weaknesses of the United States?

_____

_____

2. Citizenship Why did some people insist on the addition of a bill of rights to the Constitution?

_____

_____

3. Constitutional Heritage How does the Constitution protect citizens' rights?

_____

_____

THINKING CRITICALLY

1. Making Generalizations Why might some people have thought of the new nation as the "Dis-United States" in 1787? Explain.

_____

_____

2. Decision Making Would you have been a Federalist or Antifederalist if you had been a citizen when the Constitution was presented for ratification? Explain.

_____

_____

WRITING ABOUT HISTORY

Explaining Imagine that you are a poor farmer living during the period when the Articles of Confederation were in effect. You have just discovered that the government will not provide you with debt relief. Write a speech to tell other farmers why you think it is important to let the government know your needs.

_____

_____

_____

IDENTIFYING TERMS Choose the term or name that correctly matches each definition.

c (p. 223) **1.** set of laws that determine the duties of the government

a (p. 226) **2.** official approval

e (p. 233) **3.** low economic activity and high unemployment

b (p. 240) **4.** distribution of power between states and the central government

d (p. 243) **5.** series of essays that supported the Constitution

a. ratification

b. federalism

c. constitution

d. *Federalist Papers*

e. depression

UNDERSTANDING MAIN IDEAS

1. On which English laws did Americans base their political ideas for government?

American political ideas were based on the Magna Carta and the English Bill of Rights.

2. How could new states be created under the Northwest Ordinance?

When a portion of the Northwest Territory had at least 60,000 free inhabitants, the settlers could draft their own constitution and petition Congress to be admitted to the Union as a state.

3. How did the Articles of Confederation interfere with interstate commerce?

The Articles had no authority to regulate interstate commerce States adopted trade policies that were beneficial to their own interests. These policies varied from state to state and made trade between states difficult.

4. How did the writers of the Constitution address the concerns of Antifederalists?

The writers added 10 amendments, called the Bill of Rights, to represent the protection of individual liberties for citizens of the United States.

REVIEWING THEMES

1. Global Relations How did England and Spain take advantage of the weaknesses of the United States?

Britain closed many of its ports to American ships and imposed high tariffs on American goods sold in Britain. Spain limited U.S. trade on the lower Mississippi River.

2. Citizenship Why did some people insist on the addition of a bill of rights to the Constitution?

Some Antifederalists thought that without a bill of rights the Constitution did not adequately protect personal liberties.

3. Constitutional Heritage How does the Constitution protect citizens' rights?

The Constitution prevents any branch of government from becoming too powerful by distributing authority. For example, the framers gave Congress the power to propose and pass bills into law, but also gave the president the power to veto congressional legislation.

THINKING CRITICALLY

1. Making Generalizations Why might some people have thought of the new nation as the "Dis-United States" in 1787? Explain.

The Confederation Congress was powerless to correct the U.S. trade imbalance with Britain because it had no authority to establish tariffs. Many states focused more on improving their own commerce than on cooperating to improve the trade position of the country as a whole.

2. Decision Making Would you have been a Federalist or Antifederalist if you had been a citizen when the Constitution was presented for ratification? Explain.

Federalists should argue that the Constitution provided a good balance of power and reflected a careful compromise between a variety of political opinions. Antifederalists could argue that the Convention delegates had exceeded their authority in creating an entirely new government, that the Constitution gave too much power to the central government, or that the Constitution needed a bill of rights.

WRITING ABOUT HISTORY

Explaining Imagine that you are a poor farmer living during the period when the Articles of Confederation were in effect. You have just discovered that the government will not provide you with debt relief. Write a speech to tell other farmers why you think it is important to let the government know your needs.

Speeches should explain farmers' problems, such as taxes, debt, and being forced to sell their property. Speeches should address the problems with paper money and inflation. Speeches should persuade farmers that the newly formed government should be interested in these problems.

Chapter Tutorial

Citizenship and the Constitution

IDENTIFYING TERMS Choose the term or name that correctly matches each definition.

_____ **1.** allows Congress to stretch its delegated powers

_____ **2.** to bring charges against a president

_____ **3.** nonlegislative commands that have the force of law

_____ **4.** order that authorizes a search

_____ **5.** to send back to the country of origin

a. impeach

b. search warrant

c. deport

d. executive orders

e. elastic clause

UNDERSTANDING MAIN IDEAS

1. What are concurrent powers, delegated powers, and reserved powers?

_____

_____

2. Identify and briefly describe the function of each branch of the federal government.

_____

_____

3. According to the Fifth, Sixth, Seventh, and Eighth Amendments, what rights are held by people accused of crimes?

_____

_____

4. How can citizens become involved in their communities and governments?

_____

_____

REVIEWING THEMES

1. Citizenship Identify the different requirements for holding office and the term lengths for members of the House of Representatives and Senate.

_____

_____

2. Constitutional Heritage What did the writers of the Constitution do to prevent any one branch of the government from becoming too powerful?

_____

_____

3. Culture How do the rights of U.S. citizens differ from the rights of legal immigrants?

_____

_____

THINKING CRITICALLY

1. Drawing Inferences Do you think that any one branch of the U.S. government has more power than the others? Explain your answer.

_____

_____

2. Evaluating Which of the five freedoms provided by the First Amendment most affects your life?

_____

_____

WRITING ABOUT HISTORY

Informing Imagine that you have just come to the United States as a legal immigrant. Create a study plan for the naturalization process. Include a list of the rights, responsibilities, and aspects of U.S. history that you think you should know in order to become a U.S. citizen.

_____

_____

_____

_____

IDENTIFYING TERMS Choose the term or name that correctly matches each definition.

e (p. 257) **1.** allows Congress to stretch its delegated powers

a (p. 259) **2.** to bring charges against a president

d (p. 259) **3.** nonlegislative commands that have the force of law

b (p. 286) **4.** order that authorizes a search

c (p. 291) **5.** to send back to the country of origin

a. impeach

b. search warrant

c. deport

d. executive orders

e. elastic clause

UNDERSTANDING MAIN IDEAS

1. What are concurrent powers, delegated powers, and reserved powers?

Concurrent powers are those shared between the states and the federal government. Delegated powers are those granted to the federal government by the Constitution. Reserved powers are those held by the state governments or by the people themselves.

2. Identify and briefly describe the function of each branch of the federal government.

The legislative branch makes laws, the executive branch enforces them, and the judicial branch reviews laws and hears court cases.

3. According to the Fifth, Sixth, Seventh, and Eighth Amendments, what rights are held by people accused of crimes?

These amendments provide the accused with the right to due process, or the fair application of the law.

4. How can citizens become involved in their communities and governments?

Citizens can become involved by voting, by joining interest groups, by campaigning for candidates, and by volunteering for community service.

REVIEWING THEMES

1. **Citizenship** Identify the different requirements for holding office and the term lengths for members of the House of Representatives and Senate.

House members must be at least 25 years old, U.S. citizens for seven or more years, and residents of the state from which they are elected. Their term lasts two years. Senators must be at least 30 years old, U.S. citizens for nine or more years, and residents of the state they represent. Their term lasts six years. There are no federal restrictions on the number of terms someone may serve in Congress.

2. **Constitutional Heritage** What did the writers of the Constitution do to prevent any one branch of the government from becoming too powerful?

The writers of the Constitution attempted to prevent any branch of government from becoming too powerful by dividing power between the branches and giving each a check. For example, the president has to get Senate approval for Supreme Court appointments and treaties.

3. **Culture** How do the rights of U.S. citizens differ from the rights of legal immigrants?

Legal immigrants cannot vote or hold public office. The U.S. government also has the right to deport any immigrant who breaks the law.

THINKING CRITICALLY

1. **Drawing Inferences** Do you think that any one branch of the U.S. government has more power than the others? Explain your answer.

Answers should describe the powers of each branch and explain why that function is most important. Students should address checks and balances on each branch.

2. **Evaluating** Which of the five freedoms provided by the First Amendment most affects your life?

Students should pick one of the five freedoms—the freedom of religion, speech, the press, assembly, and petition—and discuss its significance.

WRITING ABOUT HISTORY

Informing Imagine that you have just come to the United States as a legal immigrant. Create a study plan for the naturalization process. Include a list of the rights, responsibilities, and aspects of U.S. history that you think you should know in order to become a U.S. citizen.

Study plans should include an overview of the federal government, of the three branches of government and their functions, of the Constitution; and a list of the rights in the Bill of Rights. Study plans should also include the responsibilities of citizens, such as obeying authority, paying taxes, serving in the military, serving on juries, and voting in elections.

CHAPTER 10 — Chapter Tutorial

Launching the Nation

IDENTIFYING TERMS Choose the term or name that correctly matches each definition.

_____ **1.** people who buy bonds at low prices hoping the value will rise later

_____ **2.** made a treaty with Spain that reopened port of New Orleans

_____ **3.** tried to convince Americans to support France

_____ **4.** wanted to protect powers of the states

_____ **5.** groups that help elect officials and shape government policy

a. Edmond Genet

b. political parties

c. speculators

d. Thomas Pinckney

e. Thomas Jefferson

UNDERSTANDING MAIN IDEAS

1. How did Congress organize executive branch after Washington took office?

_____

_____

2. Did Hamilton and Jefferson agree in their attitudes toward democracy? Explain.

_____

_____

3. How did the Whiskey Rebellion begin? What was Washington's response to it?

_____

_____

4. Why did Adams pursue peace with France following the XYZ affair?

_____

_____

Chapter 10 Tutorial, continued

REVIEWING THEMES

1. Global Relations What was U.S. foreign policy according to the Neutrality Proclamation? Why did the United States make and follow such a policy?

_____

_____

2. Constitutional Heritage Why were Adams and Jefferson elected president and vice president at the same time even though they were in different political parties?

_____

_____

3. Economics What did Hamilton believe the government should do about the federal debt?

_____

_____

THINKING CRITICALLY

1. Supporting a Point of View Do you support strict or loose construction of the Constitution? Explain.

_____

_____

2. Analyzing Information Does the advice George Washington gave to the nation when he left the presidency apply to the United States today? Explain your answer.

_____

_____

WRITING ABOUT HISTORY

Expressing Imagine that you live in the late 1700s. Write a detailed table of contents for a book about Republican Motherhood.

_____

_____

_____

_____

IDENTIFYING TERMS Choose the term or name that correctly matches each definition.

c (p. 305) **1.** people who buy bonds at low prices hoping the value will rise later

d (p. 313) **2.** made a treaty with Spain that reopened port of New Orleans

a (p. 312) **3.** tried to convince Americans to support France

e (p. 306) **4.** wanted to protect powers of the states

b (p. 319) **5.** groups that help elect officials and shape government policy

a. Edmond Genet

b. political parties

c. speculators

d. Thomas Pinckney

e. Thomas Jefferson

UNDERSTANDING MAIN IDEAS

1. How did Congress organize executive branch after Washington took office?

Congress created several executive departments, each specializing in a different area of national policy.

2. Did Hamilton and Jefferson agree in their attitudes toward democracy? Explain.

No—Hamilton had little faith in the common person, while Jefferson believed in the power of the majority.

3. How did the Whiskey Rebellion begin? What was Washington's response to it?

The rebellion began when farmers refused to pay the tax imposed on U.S.—made whiskey in 1794. Washington ordered several states to call out their militia, assembling an army of more than 13,000 soldiers.

4. Why did Adams pursue peace with France following the XYZ affair?

Adams believed that many people in the United States and France were opposed to war. He was also concerned about the expense of a war.

REVIEWING THEMES

1. Global Relations What was U.S. foreign policy according to the Neutrality Proclamation? Why did the United States make and follow such a policy?

The United States would remain neutral toward all nations at war in Europe. It was a plan that President Washington thought was the safest and most reasonable for the new country.

2. Constitutional Heritage Why were Adams and Jefferson elected president and vice president at the same time even though they were in different political parties?

Under the rules of the Constitution at that time, the second-place finisher in a presidential election became vice president even if that person was not of the same political party as the president.

3. Economics What did Hamilton believe the government should do about the federal debt?

Hamilton wanted the government to pay off the national debt, including that debt in the form of bonds.

THINKING CRITICALLY

1. Supporting a Point of View Do you support strict or loose construction of the Constitution? Explain.

Supporters of strict construction of the Constitution believed that the federal government could only do what the Constitution specifically said it could do. They should argue that the elastic clause was to be used only under limited circumstances. Loose constructionists believed that the federal government could take reasonable actions that the Constitution did not specifically forbid it from taking and that the elastic clause was to be flexible so that the government could react appropriately to change.

2. Analyzing Information Does the advice George Washington gave to the nation when he left the presidency apply to the United States today? Explain your answer.

Washington's advice warned the nation about the greatest threats to the American republic: public debt, dangerous foreign alliances, and political divisions at home. Answers should evaluate this advice as it relates to the United States today.

WRITING ABOUT HISTORY

Expressing Imagine that you live in the late 1700s. Write a detailed table of contents for a book about Republican Motherhood.

Expressing Imagine that you live in the late 1700s. Write a detailed table of contents for a book about Republican Motherhood. Table of contents should include a definition of Republican Motherhood. Chapters should include promoters of Republican Motherhood, expectations, and need for education.

CHAPTER 11

Chapter Tutorial

The Expanding Nation

IDENTIFYING TERMS Choose the term or name that correctly matches each definition.

_____ **1.** allows the Supreme Court to declare laws unconstitutional

_____ **2.** co-leader of an expedition to the West

_____ **3.** practice of forcing people to serve in the army or navy

_____ **4.** banned trade with Britain and France

_____ **5.** peace treaty that ended the War of 1812

a. impressment

b. Treaty of Ghent

c. William Clark

d. Non-Intercourse Act

e. judicial review

UNDERSTANDING MAIN IDEAS

1. Which Federalist policies did Thomas Jefferson leave in place when he took office?

_____

_____

2. What made New Orleans and the Mississippi River important to the United States?

_____

_____

3. What dangers did U.S. ships face while crossing the Atlantic Ocean during the early 1800s?

_____

_____

4. What were Tecumseh's goals for American Indians of the Northwest Territory, the South, and the Mississippi Valley?

_____

_____

5. What were the strengths and weaknesses of the U.S. Navy in the War of 1812?

_____

_____

REVIEWING THEMES

1. Constitutional Heritage What precedent did Chief Justice John Marshall set in his *Marbury* v. *Madison* ruling?

_____

_____

2. Geography Why was the United States interested in exploring land west of its boundaries?

_____

_____

3. Global Relations What problems did U.S. merchant ships face offshore from the Barbary States?

_____

_____

THINKING CRITICALLY

1. Drawing Conclusions What do you think were Jefferson's reasons for planning a simple inauguration?

_____

_____

2. Analyzing Information What made President Jefferson reluctant to approve the Louisiana Purchase?

_____

_____

WRITING ABOUT HISTORY

Explaining Imagine that you are John Marshall, the chief justice of the United States. Explain to President Jefferson why you made the decision to deny William Marbury his judgeship.

_____

_____

_____

_____

IDENTIFYING TERMS Choose the term or name that correctly matches each definition.

e (p. 337) **1.** allows the Supreme Court to declare laws unconstitutional

c (p. 341) **2.** co-leader of an expedition to the West

a (p. 345) **3.** practice of forcing people to serve in the army or navy

d (p. 346) **4.** banned U.S. trade with Britain and France

b (p. 355) **5.** peace treaty that ended the War of 1812

a. impressment

b. Treaty of Ghent

c. William Clark

d. Non-Intercourse Act

e. judicial review

UNDERSTANDING MAIN IDEAS

1. Which Federalist policies did Thomas Jefferson leave in place when he took office?

Jefferson kept the Federalist-supported Bank of the United States and retained some Federalists in their government positions.

2. What made New Orleans and the Mississippi River important to the United States?

Control of the Mississippi River and the seaport of New Orleans was vital to U.S. trade and to the future westward expansion of the United States.

3. What dangers did U.S. ships face while crossing the Atlantic Ocean during the early 1800s?

The British and French navies captured many American merchant ships. In addition, the Barbary States practiced piracy and held captives for ransom.

4. What were Tecumseh's goals for American Indians of the Northwest Territory, the South, and the Mississippi Valley?

Tecumseh wanted to unite the American Indians of the Northwest Territory, the South, and the eastern Mississippi Valley into a single confederation to oppose American settlement.

5. What were the strengths and weaknesses of the U.S. Navy in the War of 1812?

The navy had fewer than 20 ships and none as powerful as the greatest British warships, but the navy also had well-trained sailors and its warships were more powerful than most of the British ships of the same size. The United States also used privateers to attack British merchant ships.

REVIEWING THEMES

1. **Constitutional Heritage** What precedent did Chief Justice John Marshall set in his *Marbury* v. *Madison* ruling?

Marshall established the principle of judicial review, the power of the Supreme Court to declare an act of Congress to be unconstitutional and therefore without any legal authority.

2. **Geography** Why was the United States interested in exploring land west of its boundaries?

The United States knew little about western American Indians or the land they occupied. Jefferson also wanted to see if there was a river route that could be taken to the Pacific Ocean.

3. **Global Relations** What problems did U.S. merchant ships face offshore from the Barbary States?

U.S. merchant ships were at the mercy of pirates whose fleets were operated by the kingdoms of the Barbary States. The United States government refused to make payments to the Barbary States to prevent them from taking U.S. hostages.

THINKING CRITICALLY

1. **Drawing Conclusions** What do you think were Jefferson's reasons for planning a simple inauguration?

Jefferson's reasons might include wanting to demonstrate his democratic views on government and to prove how easily power could change hands in the United States.

2. **Analyzing Information** What made President Jefferson reluctant to approve the Louisiana Purchase?

Jefferson reluctantly approved the Louisiana Purchase because as a strict constructionist, he did not believe that the Constitution granted the federal government's executive branch the power to bring territories such as Louisiana into the United States.

WRITING ABOUT HISTORY

Explaining Imagine that you are John Marshall, the chief justice of the United States. Explain to President Jefferson why you made the decision to deny William Marbury his judgeship.

Marshall should explain that Marbury had the legal right to his judgeship, but the Supreme Court did not have the power to force Madison to give Marbury the position. Marshall should explain that the Judiciary Act of 1789 had given the Supreme Court powers that were, in fact, unconstitutional. Marshall should explain the principle of judicial review.

A New National Identity

IDENTIFYING TERMS Choose the term or name that correctly matches each definition.

_____ **1.** first federal road project

_____ **2.** President Jackson's informal group of advisers

_____ **3.** dispute between state and federal governments

_____ **4.** first principal chief of the Cherokee Nation

_____ **5.** gave Florida to the U.S.

a. John Ross

b. Cumberland Road

c. nullification crisis

d. Adams-Onís Treaty

e. kitchen cabinet

UNDERSTANDING MAIN IDEAS

1. Why is Monroe's presidency known as the "Era of Good Feelings"?

_____

_____

2. How did the availability of new transportation systems affect the United States?

_____

_____

3. What was the controversy surrounding the election of 1824?

_____

_____

4. What prompted the U.S. government to begin an Indian Removal policy?

_____

_____

5. How did Europeans view the writing of Washington Irving?

_____

_____

_____

Chapter 12 Tutorial, continued

REVIEWING THEMES

1. Global Relations What land disputes did the United States have with British Canada and Spain?

_____

_____

2. Citizenship Why did Andrew Jackson's supporters claim that John Quincy Adams was unfairly elected president?

_____

_____

3. Constitutional Heritage What was the Supreme Court's ruling in *Worcester* v. *Georgia*?

_____

_____

THINKING CRITICALLY

1. Evaluating Would you have supported Jackson's use of the spoils system? Explain your answer.

_____

_____

2. Drawing Inferences What made it important for Americans to develop their own culture in the 1820s?

_____

_____

WRITING ABOUT HISTORY

Expressing Imagine that you are a newspaper editor living in the 1820s or 1830s. Write an editorial letting your readers know how you feel about Jacksonian Democracy's effect on white men, women, and free African Americans.

_____

_____

_____

_____

A New National Identity

IDENTIFYING TERMS Choose the term or name that correctly matches each definition.

b *(p. 371)* **1.** first federal road project

e *(p. 376)* **2.** President Jackson's informal group of advisers

c *(p. 377)* **3.** dispute between state and federal governments

a *(p. 382)* **4.** first principal chief of the Cherokee Nation

d *(p. 366)* **5.** gave Florida to the U.S.

a. John Ross

b. Cumberland Road

c. nullification crisis

d. Adams-Onís Treaty

e. kitchen cabinet

UNDERSTANDING MAIN IDEAS

1. Why is Monroe's presidency known as the "Era of Good Feelings"?

After the War of 1812, the United States experienced a period of relative peace and national pride. Members of Monroe's presidency resolved ongoing conflicts with foreign powers.

2. How did the availability of new transportation systems affect the United States?

With the construction of roads and canals, transportation and trade became quicker, easier, and cheaper.

3. What was the controversy surrounding the election of 1824?

Jackson received the most popular votes but did not have enough electoral votes to win office. Under the Constitution, the House of Representatives had to determine the winner. Speaker of the House Henry Clay influenced the vote by backing Adams. When the House chose Adams as president, Jackson's supporters claimed that Adams had made a "corrupt bargain" with Clay. These accusations increased after Adams appointed Clay secretary of state.

4. What prompted the U.S. government to begin an Indian Removal policy?

The government wanted Indians to move to lands in the West in order to clear the land for American settlers.

5. How did Europeans view the writing of Washington Irving?

Irving was one of the first American writers to gain respect in Europe.

REVIEWING THEMES

1. Global Relations What land disputes did the United States have with British Canada and Spain?

After the War of 1812, both the United States and British Canada wanted to maintain fishing rights and navies on the Great Lakes. The United States's dispute with Spain was over Florida. Some Americans wanted to move there, while some southerners were upset by the actions of the Seminole Indians, who often helped runaway slaves and sometime raided U.S. settlements.

2. Citizenship Why did Andrew Jackson's supporters claim that John Quincy Adams was unfairly elected president?

Jackson's supporters claimed that Adams made a "corrupt bargain" with Clay. As Speaker of the House, Clay supported Adams and Adams later made Clay his secretary of state.

3. Constitutional Heritage What was the Supreme Court's ruling in *Worcester* v. *Georgia*?

The Court ruled that the Cherokee nation was a distinct community over which Georgia could have no authority. The Court ruled that only the federal government had authority over the Cherokee.

THINKING CRITICALLY

1. Evaluating Would you have supported Jackson's use of the spoils system? Explain your answer.

Jackson rewarded some of his supporters with government jobs—a practice known as the spoils system. Answers should point out that Jackson replaced fewer than one fifth of federal officeholders.

2. Drawing Inferences What made it important for Americans to develop their own culture in the 1820s?

After the War of 1812, Americans felt a need to create a new national identity that was uniquely American.

WRITING ABOUT HISTORY

Expressing Imagine that you are a newspaper editor living in the 1820s or 1830s. Write an editorial letting your readers know how you feel about Jacksonian Democracy's effect on white men, women, and free African Americans.

Editorials should discuss how the expansion of suffrage for white men increased their participation in politics and government. Women were not allowed to vote in any state and free African Americans could not vote in most states.

Name _____ Class _____ Date _____

IDENTIFYING TERMS Choose the term or name that correctly matches each definition.

_____ **1.** tools designed to produce goods or do work

_____ **2.** refusing to work until employers meet workers' demands

_____ **3.** inventor who developed a steam-powered boat

_____ **4.** developed a new harvesting machine

_____ **5.** invented the telegraph

a. strikes

b. Cyrus McCormick

c. Samuel Morse

d. Robert Fulton

e. technology

UNDERSTANDING MAIN IDEAS

1. How did Eli Whitney's ideas contribute to manufacturing in the United States?

_____

_____

2. What benefits arose from the use of the spinning jenny?

_____

_____

3. Describe the Lowell system.

_____

_____

4. Identify the advantages and disadvantages of railroads in the United States.

_____

_____

5. How did farmers benefit from McCormick's reaper?

_____

_____

Chapter 13 Tutorial, continued

REVIEWING THEMES

1. Government What was the importance of *Gibbons* v. *Ogden*?

_____

_____

2. Science, Technology & Society What changes did the Industrial Revolution bring to the people living in the Northeast?

_____

_____

3. Economics How did the Transportation Revolution affect the U.S. economy?

_____

_____

THINKING CRITICALLY

1. Decision Making Would you have rather worked under the Rhode Island system or the Lowell system? Explain your answer.

_____

_____

2. Identifying Cause and Effect What impact did the telegraph have on communication?

_____

_____

WRITING ABOUT HISTORY

Informing Imagine that you are a mill worker and the leader of a trade union that is about to go on strike. Write a pamphlet that explains to union members why a strike is necessary.

_____

_____

_____

_____

IDENTIFYING TERMS Choose the term or name that correctly matches each definition.

e <u>(p. 401)</u> **1.** tools designed to produce goods or do work

a <u>(p. 408)</u> **2.** refusing to work until employers meet workers' demands

d <u>(p. 411)</u> **3.** inventor who developed a steam-powered boat

b <u>(p. 418)</u> **4.** developed a new harvesting machine

c <u>(p. 415)</u> **5.** invented the telegraph

a. strikes

b. Cyrus McCormick

c. Samuel Morse

d. Robert Fulton

e. technology

UNDERSTANDING MAIN IDEAS

1. How did Eli Whitney's ideas contribute to manufacturing in the United States?

Whitney's ideas contributed to the faster manufacturing of goods through the use of interchangeable parts and mass production.

2. What benefits arose from the use of the spinning jenny?

The spinning jenny increased the speed of textile production by allowing one worker to spin large amounts of thread.

3. Describe the Lowell system.

The Lowell system was a combination of employing young unmarried women and doing spinning and weaving in one mill.

4. Identify the advantages and disadvantages of railroads in the United States.

Advantages included faster travel, linking of communities, and greater freight transportation. Disadvantages included train wrecks.

5. How did farmers benefit from McCormick's reaper?

The reaper cut down wheat much more quickly and efficiently.

REVIEWING THEMES

1. Government What was the importance of *Gibbons* v. *Ogden*?

It established the supremacy of the national government in the control of interstate commerce and expanded the definition of commerce.

2. Science, Technology & Society What changes did the Industrial Revolution bring to the people living in the Northeast?

Families and unmarried women began working in textile mills. Workers became concerned about the growth of factories, lower wages, and increased competition for jobs.

3. Economics How did the Transportation Revolution affect the U.S. economy?

The Transportation Revolution helped create a boom in business across the country, particularly by speeding travel and reducing shipping time and shipping rates between the East and West.

THINKING CRITICALLY

1. Decision Making Would you have rather worked under the Rhode Island system or the Lowell system? Explain your answer.

The Rhode Island system included hiring families and dividing factory work into simple tasks. Children worked with their parent. The Lowell system included spinning and weaving in one mill and employing young unmarried women, who lived together. Daily life was carefully regulated and mill machinery was often dangerous.

2. Identifying Cause and Effect What impact did the telegraph have on communication?

The telegraph connected cities throughout the United States by sending and receiving information for the government, newspaper, businesses, and private citizens.

WRITING ABOUT HISTORY

Informing Imagine that you are a mill worker and the leader of a trade union that is about to go on strike. Write a pamphlet that explains to union members why a strike is necessary.

The pamphlet should be persuasive and directed to all mill workers. The pamphlet should describe mill conditions, either in the Lowell or Rhode Island system. The pamphlet should discuss negative working conditions and dangers associated with mill machinery.

CHAPTER 14

Chapter Tutorial

Agricultural Changes in the South

IDENTIFYING TERMS Choose the term or name that correctly matches each definition.

_____ **1.** built a machine that removed seeds from cotton fibers   **a.** factors

_____ **2.** region that grew most of the country's cotton crop   **b.** yeomen

_____ **3.** managed the cotton trade   **c.** cotton belt

_____ **4.** owners of small farms   **d.** folktales

_____ **5.** stories with a moral   **e.** Eli Whitney

UNDERSTANDING MAIN IDEAS

1. Why did slavery seem to decline after the American Revolution?

_____

_____

2. What caused the cotton boom?

_____

_____

3. Identify the types of southern factories that existed in the 1800s.

_____

_____

4. Describe the cultural and social life of rural white southerners.

_____

_____

5. Were family ties important to enslaved people? Explain your answer.

_____

_____

REVIEWING THEMES

1. Science, Technology & Society How did the invention of the cotton gin increase southern dependence on slave labor?

_____

_____

2. Economics What impact did industrialization have on the southern economy?

_____

_____

3. Culture What effects did slavery have on African American culture?

_____

_____

THINKING CRITICALLY

1. Drawing Conclusions What problems might result from an economy that is heavily dependent upon agriculture?

_____

_____

2. Comparing How did the lives of poor whites compare to the lives of slaves?

_____

_____

WRITING ABOUT HISTORY

Persuading If you were a southern farmer living in the early to mid-1800s, which food and non-food crops would you advise a fellow farmer to grow, and why?

_____

_____

_____

_____

Agricultural Changes in the South

IDENTIFYING TERMS Choose the term or name that correctly matches each definition.

_e (p. 426)_ **1.** built a machine that removed seeds from cotton fibers

_c (p. 427)_ **2.** region that grew most of the country's cotton crop

_a (p. 429)_ **3.** managed the cotton trade

_b (p. 434)_ **4.** owners of small farms

_d (p. 442)_ **5.** stories with a moral

a. factors

b. yeomen

c. cotton belt

d. folktales

e. Eli Whitney

UNDERSTANDING MAIN IDEAS

1. Why did slavery seem to decline after the American Revolution?

Some Revolutionary leaders believed that a nation founded on the ideal of liberty could not justify enslaving people. The drop in indigo, rice, and tobacco prices in the late 1700s also led many landowners to need fewer slaves and to free them.

2. What caused the cotton boom?

The expanding British and U.S. textile industries increased the demand for cotton and the cotton gin made growing cotton very profitable.

3. Identify the types of southern factories that existed in the 1800s.

Southern factories primarily served the needs of farmers. Factories manufactured rope, cut lumber, and made iron products.

4. Describe the cultural and social life of rural white southerners.

Religion was central to southern social life. People often saw neighbors only at special church functions, such as revivals and socials.

5. Were family ties important to enslaved people? Explain your answer.

The family was the most important unit of slave communities. People held as slaves feared being sold to another plantation and separated from their families.

REVIEWING THEMES

1. Science, Technology & Society How did the invention of the cotton gin increase southern dependence on slave labor?

Whitney's cotton gin sparked a boom in the growing of cotton, which required many field hands. Rather than hire workers through a wage-labor system, planters began to rely more heavily than ever on the slave system.

2. Economics What impact did industrialization have on the southern economy?

Industrialization in the South lagged behind the North. Most of the factories in the South were built to process crops.

3. Culture What effects did slavery have on African American culture?

People held as slaves worked hard to maintain strong ties to their heritage. African Americans passed down stories about family history, customs, and traditions of life in Africa, and they told folktales. Religion was another important aspect of slave culture and those held as slaves often expressed their religious beliefs through the singing of spirituals.

THINKING CRITICALLY

1. Drawing Conclusions What problems might result from an economy that is heavily dependent upon agriculture?

Problems might include dependence on foreign markets and products, wearing out the soil, and slow industrialization.

2. Comparing How did the lives of poor whites compare to the lives of slaves?

Poor whites were landless and looked down upon by other white people. They lived on lands unsuitable for producing cash crops. Many survived by hunting, fishing, raising small gardens, and doing odd jobs for money. Slaves were also discriminated against by white people. Poor whites however, were free. They were not considered another person's property.

WRITING ABOUT HISTORY

Persuading If you were a southern farmer living in the early to mid-1800s, which food and non-food crops would you advise a fellow farmer to grow, and why?

A southern farmer would recommend growing cotton as a cash crop and corn as a food crop. Other crops would depend somewhat on location of the farm, but other food crops might include rice, sugarcane, sweet potatoes, and wheat. Nonfood crops could include flax, hemp, and tobacco.

CHAPTER 15

Chapter Tutorial

New Movements in America

IDENTIFYING TERMS Choose the term or name that correctly matches each definition.

_____ **1.** groups of people working to establish a perfect society

_____ **2.** U.S. citizens who opposed immigration

_____ **3.** reformer of prison systems who also helped the mentally ill

_____ **4.** the idea that people could rise above material things

_____ **5.** well-known speaker for the Anti-Slavery Society and women's right

a. Lucy Stone

b. utopian communities

c. transcendentalism

d. nativists

e. Dorothea Dix

UNDERSTANDING MAIN IDEAS

1. What was the message of the romantic movement?

_____

_____

2. Why did nativists feel threatened by immigrants?

_____

_____

3. Why were many middle-class women active in reform movements during the 1800s?

_____

_____

4. Who were the abolitionists, and what did they hope to achieve for enslaved African Americans?

_____

_____

5. What led female abolitionists to become active in the women's rights movement?

_____

_____

REVIEWING THEMES

1. Culture Why did people try to establish utopian communities in the early to mid-1800s?

_____

_____

2. Geography What economic and political factors encouraged German and Irish people to immigrate to the United States in the mid-1800s?

_____

_____

3. Citizenship Explain how Frederick Douglass and Harriet Tubman worked to end slavery.

_____

_____

THINKING CRITICALLY

1. Drawing Conclusions How did the Second Great Awakening affect the abolition movement?

_____

_____

2. Evaluating Why do you think people wanted to become part of the Underground Railroad?

_____

_____

WRITING ABOUT HISTORY

Persuading Imagine that you are an immigrant in the mid-1800s. Write a pamphlet to convince nativists to end their fight against immigration.

_____

_____

_____

_____

IDENTIFYING TERMS Choose the term or name that correctly matches each definition.

b (p. 454) **1.** groups of people working to establish a perfect society

d (p. 459) **2.** U.S. citizens who opposed immigration

e (p. 462) **3.** reformer of prison systems who also helped the mentally ill

c (p. 454) **4.** the idea that people could rise above material things

a (p. 479) **5.** well-known speaker for the Anti-Slavery Society and women's right

a. Lucy Stone

b. utopian communities

c. transcendentalism

d. nativists

e. Dorothea Dix

UNDERSTANDING MAIN IDEAS

1. What was the message of the romantic movement?

Each individual brings a unique perspective to the world.

2. Why did nativists feel threatened by immigrants?

They feared economic competition from immigrants and felt threatened by immigrants' different cultures and religious beliefs.

3. Why were many middle-class women active in reform movements during the 1800s?

Many middle-class women did not work outside the home and had domestic servants to do housework. This gave them more time to become active in reform movements.

4. Who were the abolitionists, and what did they hope to achieve for enslaved African Americans?

Abolitionists were reformers who opposed slavery and wanted to emancipate, or free, all people held as slaves.

5. What led female abolitionists to become active in the women's rights movement?

Female abolitionists found they had to defend their right to speak in public.

REVIEWING THEMES

1. Culture Why did people try to establish utopian communities in the early to mid-1800s?

Some people wanted to create perfect societies on Earth either for religious reasons or for social reasons

2. Geography What economic and political factors encouraged German and Irish people to immigrate to the United States in the mid-1800s?

Many Germans were fleeing a failed political revolution in the German states, while large numbers of Irish were trying to escape the terrible Irish potato famine and the economic crisis that accompanied it.

3. Citizenship Explain how Frederick Douglass and Harriet Tubman worked to end slavery.

Douglass spoke about the horrors of slavery at abolitionist meetings and wrote a newspaper and several autobiographies. Tubman led slaves to freedom on the Underground Railroad.

THINKING CRITICALLY

1. Drawing Conclusions How did the Second Great Awakening affect the abolition movement?

Some ministers during the Second Great Awakening taught their followers that slavery was morally wrong and inspired increased support for abolition.

2. Evaluating Why do you think people wanted to become part of the Underground Railroad?

Participants probably felt that they were helping to fight a great injustice and doing good deeds by helping slaves escape to freedom.

WRITING ABOUT HISTORY

Persuading Imagine that you are an immigrant in the mid-1800s. Write a pamphlet to convince nativists to end their fight against immigration.

Students might mention that immigrants actually help the economy improve by filling the need for cheap labor. They could also note that the United States was founded by immigrants from different countries and that other immigrants also deserve a chance to contribute. Other points might include the right to freedom of religion and the benefits of having a diverse society.

Expanding West

IDENTIFYING TERMS Choose the term or name that correctly matches each definition.

_____ 1. Spanish colonists in California

_____ 2. an old mission in San Antonio

_____ 3. an independent nation whose capital was Houston

_____ 4. event at which mountain men met to trade and socialize

_____ 5. popular California colony near the Sacramento River

a. Republic of Texas

b. rendezvous

c. Californios

d. Sutter's Fort

e. Alamo

UNDERSTANDING MAIN IDEAS

1. What did Father Hidalgo hope to gain by seeking Mexico's independence from Spain?

_____

_____

2. What did the Mexican government hire *empresarios* to do?

_____

_____

3. Why was President Jackson hesitant about annexing Texas?

_____

_____

4. Why did Cayuse Indians become angry with Marcus and Narcissa Whitman?

_____

_____

5. What was important about the art work created by artists who traveled to the West?

_____

_____

Chapter 16 Tutorial, *continued*

REVIEWING THEMES

1. Citizenship Why did Texas declare its independence from Mexico?

_____

_____

2. Culture How did the policies of the Republic of Texas affect Tejanos?

_____

_____

3. Geography Why did missionaries go to Oregon country?

_____

_____

THINKING CRITICALLY

1. Drawing Conclusions Do you think the Spanish should have continued using the mission system? Explain your answer.

_____

_____

2. Identifying Cause and Effect How did the Panic of 1837 affect westward settlement?

_____

_____

WRITING ABOUT HISTORY

Creating Imagine that you are an *empresario*. Write a flyer encouraging people to move to Texas.

_____

_____

_____

_____

 CHAPTER **16**

Chapter Tutorial (Partner)

Expanding West

IDENTIFYING TERMS Choose the term or name that correctly matches each definition.

c (p. 489) **1.** Spanish colonists in California

e (p. 494) **2.** an old mission in San Antonio

a (p. 497) **3.** an independent nation whose capital was Houston

b (p. 503) **4.** event at which mountain men met to trade and socialize

d (p. 509) **5.** popular California colony near the Sacramento River

a. Republic of Texas

b. rendezvous

c. Californios

d. Sutter's Fort

e. Alamo

UNDERSTANDING MAIN IDEAS

1. What did Father Hidalgo hope to gain by seeking Mexico's independence from Spain?

He hoped to improve living conditions for poor Indians and mestizos living in New Spain.

2. What did the Mexican government hire *empresarios* to do?

The Mexican government hoped the empresarios would bring settlers to Texas.

3. Why was President Jackson hesitant about annexing Texas?

He was concerned that the annexation of Texas would add another slave state to the Union, upsetting the balance of slave and free states. Jackson also did not want to go to war with Mexico.

4. Why did Cayuse Indians become angry with Marcus and Narcissa Whitman?

The Whitmans and the settlers they attracted to their mission carried diseases to which the Cayuse were not immune. When an epidemic killed many of the Cayuse children, the Cayuse attacked the Whitmans.

5. What was important about the art work created by artists who traveled to the West?

Their work became popular in the East, shaping the way people pictured the West.

REVIEWING THEMES

1. Citizenship Why did Texas declare its independence from Mexico?

American settlers in Texas wanted to institute more local control and resented having to follow Mexican laws. Some Texans were also angered by the suspension of the Constitution of 1824 by Santa Anna.

2. Culture How did the policies of the Republic of Texas affect Tejanos?

They suffered under these policies, losing their land and political power.

3. Geography Why did missionaries go to Oregon country?

Inspired by the Second Great Awakening, the missionaries wanted to convert American Indians to Christianity.

THINKING CRITICALLY

1. Drawing Conclusions Do you think the Spanish should have continued using the mission system? Explain your answer.

Students who think the mission system should have stayed in place might mention the fact that the Indians continued to suffer after it was ended. Those who think the mission system should not have continued might mention the poor living conditions and high death rate of Indians living in the missions.

2. Identifying Cause and Effect How did the Panic of 1837 affect westward settlement?

The Panic of 1837 led many people to move west, particularly to Texas, searching for more opportunities and a better life.

WRITING ABOUT HISTORY

Creating Imagine that you are an *empresario*. Write a flyer encouraging people to move to Texas.

Students' flyers should mention the cheap or free land and the amounts available. They might also mention that the land was good for growing cotton and cattle ranching.

 **CHAPTER 17** Chapter Tutorial

Manifest Destiny and War

IDENTIFYING TERMS Choose the term or name that correctly matches each definition.

_____ **1.** led U.S. soldiers in the Rio Grande region

_____ **2.** founded the Church of Jesus Christ of Latter-Day Saints.

_____ **3.** uprising during which rebels declared California independent

_____ **4.** to search for gold

_____ **5.** granted much of Mexico's northern territory to the United States

a. Mexican Cession

b. Zachary Taylor

c. Joseph Smith

d. Bear Flag Revolt

e. prospect

UNDERSTANDING MAIN IDEAS

1. What effect did the possible annexation of Texas have on the election of 1844?

_____

_____

2. How did Mexico react to the U.S. annexation of Texas?

_____

_____

3. Why did the Mormons leave New York and move west?

_____

_____

4. What effect did the Gold Rush have on the population of California?

_____

_____

5. In what ways were Chinese miners discriminated against?

_____

_____

REVIEWING THEMES

1. Global Relations How did the United States acquire Oregon?

_____

_____

2. Culture What conflicts arose among Mexican Americans, American Indians, and American settlers in the Southwest?

_____

_____

3. Geography Where did many forty-niners and immigrants to California originally come from?

_____

_____

THINKING CRITICALLY

1. Supporting a Point of View Do you think the United States had a good reason for declaring war on Mexico? Explain your answer.

_____

_____

2. Drawing Conclusions Do you think that Taylor's experience as a military leader qualified him to be president? Explain your answer.

_____

_____

WRITING ABOUT HISTORY

Explaining Imagine that you are an American Indian living in the Southwest. Tell a story illustrating why U.S. settlers should respect your land rights and your customs.

_____

_____

_____

_____

IDENTIFYING TERMS Choose the term or name that correctly matches each definition.

b (p. 521) **1.** led U.S. soldiers in the Rio Grande region

c (p. 531) **2.** founded the Church of Jesus Christ of Latter-Day Saints.

d (p. 524) **3.** uprising during which rebels declared California independent

e (p. x) **4.** to search for gold

a (p. 526) **5.** granted much of Mexico's northern territory to the United States

a. Mexican Cession

b. Zachary Taylor

c. Joseph Smith

d. Bear Flag Revolt

e. prospect

UNDERSTANDING MAIN IDEAS

1. What effect did the possible annexation of Texas have on the election of 1844?

John Tyler made Texas into a national issue with his desire to extend the political power of the South by annexing it. However, his party, the Whigs, disagreed with him and instead selected Henry Clay as their candidate in 1844. Clay's opposition to annexation made him unpopular and he changed his policy during the campaign. Nonetheless, Clay was defeated by James K. Polk, who supported annexation whole-heartedly.

2. How did Mexico react to the U.S. annexation of Texas?

Mexico regarded Texas as a "stolen province" and resented U.S. annexation of the territory. The Mexican government then cut of all diplomatic relations and removed American settlers from California and banned further American immigration there.

3. Why did the Mormons leave New York and move west?

Mormons were persecuted for their religious beliefs and their practice of polygamy. They went west hoping to find a place where they could practice their religion without interference.

4. What effect did the Gold Rush have on the population of California?

The gold rush vastly increased California's population in a very short time. In addition, it changed the ethnic make-up of the area.

5. In what ways were Chinese miners discriminated against?

Chinese immigrants could not become U.S. citizens and were taxed as foreign miners. They were also the targets of violent attacks. In addition, they were discriminated against in the courts.

REVIEWING THEMES

1. Global Relations How did the United States acquire Oregon?

The United States acquired Oregon after settling disputes over the territory with Britan, Russia, and Spain. The dispute with Britain came closest to war. However, the two countries compromised over the boundary line and opened the way for the United States to annex Oregon.

2. Culture What conflicts arose among Mexican Americans, American Indians, and American settlers in the Southwest?

Many conflicts in the Southwest arose over the ownership of land. American settlers often wanted land that was already owned by Mexicans or settled by Indians.

3. Geography Where did many forty-niners and immigrants to California originally come from?

The majority of the forty-niners were from the United States. Others came from all over the world.

THINKING CRITICALLY

1. Supporting a Point of View Do you think the United States had a good reason for declaring war on Mexico? Explain your answer.

Students who say the U.S. reasons were good might mention Mexico's response to the annexation of Texas and the Mexican attack on Taylor at Matamoros. Students who think the United States did not have a good reason might mention the border dispute and the fact that the U.S. Army seemed to be the aggressor by sending Taylor into a disputed region.

2. Drawing Conclusions Do you think that Taylor's experience as a military leader qualified him to be president? Explain your answer.

Some may say military service prepared Taylor to make decisions and lead people. Others may say that the dictatorial power given to military leaders is out of place in the leader of a democracy.

WRITING ABOUT HISTORY

Explaining Imagine that you are an American Indian living in the Southwest. Tell a story illustrating why U.S. settlers should respect your land rights and your customs.

Students' stories should describe the Indians' customs and the fact that they had lived on the land long before American settlers had arrived. They ought to mention particular examples of times when settlers abused their customs.

CHAPTER **18**

Chapter Tutorial

A Divided Nation

IDENTIFYING TERMS Choose the term or name that correctly matches each definition.

_____ **1.** allowed escaped slaves to be arrested where slavery was illegal

_____ **2.** wrote a powerful antislavery novel published in 1852

_____ **3.** debated Lincoln seven times over issues such as slavery

_____ **4.** wrote the majority opinion in the *Dred Scott* decision

_____ **5.** act of formally withdrawing from the Union

a. Stephen Douglas

b. Harriet Beecher Stowe

c. Roger B. Taney

d. Fugitive Slave Act

e. secession

UNDERSTANDING MAIN IDEAS

1. Why did many northerners support the Wilmot Proviso?

_____

_____

2. List the five main parts of the Compromise of 1850.

_____

_____

3. What did pro-slavery groups do to influence the Kansas territorial election in 1855?

_____

_____

4. How did the Kansas-Nebraska Act affect the Democratic Party?

_____

_____

5. What was the primary difference between the constitution of the Confederate States of America and the U.S. Constitution?

_____

_____

REVIEWING THEMES

1. Geography How did the addition of the Mexican Cession to the United States create conflicts between the North and the South?

_____

_____

2. Citizenship What was the ruling in the *Dred Scott* decision?

_____

_____

3. Constitutional Heritage Why did some southern states feel that secession from the United States was legal?

_____

_____

THINKING CRITICALLY

1. Drawing Conclusions Why did southerners want to maintain a balance between the number of free and slave states?

_____

_____

2. Comparing Describe the different views expressed by Lincoln and Douglas in their debates regarding slavery and racial equality.

_____

_____

WRITING ABOUT HISTORY

Creating Imagine that you are a northerner who is opposed to the Fugitive Slave Act. Create a poster that demonstrates your views to display in your town.

_____

_____

_____

_____

A Divided Nation

IDENTIFYING TERMS Choose the term or name that correctly matches each definition.

d *(p. 556)* **1.** allowed escaped slaves to be arrested where slavery was illegal

b *(p. 557)* **2.** wrote a powerful antislavery novel published in 1852

a *(p. 567)* **3.** debated Lincoln seven times over issues such as slavery

c *(p. 566)* **4.** wrote the majority opinion in the *Dred Scott* decision

e *(p. 573)* **5.** act of formally withdrawing from the Union

a. Stephen Douglas

b. Harriet Beecher Stowe

c. Roger B. Taney

d. Fugitive Slave Act

e. secession

UNDERSTANDING MAIN IDEAS

1. Why did many northerners support the Wilmot Proviso?

Supporters of the Wilmot Proviso wanted to prevent slavery from spreading into the lands acquired in the Mexican Cession.

2. List the five main parts of the Compromise of 1850.

First, Congress admitted California as a free state. Second, the territory of New Mexico was organized and allowed to choose whether slavery would be allowed within its borders. Third, Texas gave up its claims to land east of the upper Rio Grande in exchange for the federal government assuming the debts of the Republic of Texas. Fourth, the slave trade was banned in the national capital. Fifth, the Fugitive Slave Act was passed.

3. What did pro-slavery groups do to influence the Kansas territorial election in 1855?

Pro-slavery activists entered Kansas from Missouri, voted in favor of slavery in the territorial elections, and returned to their real homes.

4. How did the Kansas-Nebraska Act affect the Democratic Party?

The Kansas-Nebraska Act led many northern antislavery Democrats to leave the party or split themselves from the southern Democrats.

5. What was the primary difference between the constitution of the Confederate States of America and the U.S. Constitution?

The Confederate constitution specifically endorsed slavery.

REVIEWING THEMES

1. Geography How did the addition of the Mexican Cession to the United States create conflicts between the North and the South?

Northerners and southerners became divided over the question of whether slavery would be allowed in the lands of the Mexican Cession.

2. Citizenship What was the ruling in the *Dred Scott* decision?

The Supreme Court ruled that African Americans were not citizens of the United States and thus were not entitled to constitutional rights. It also declared the Missouri compromise unconstitutional and said that Congress could not ban slavery in any federal territory.

3. Constitutional Heritage Why did some southern states feel that secession from the United States was legal?

Some southerners claimed that since the original states had joined the Union voluntarily, any state should be allowed to leave the Union voluntarily.

THINKING CRITICALLY

1. Drawing Conclusions Why did southerners want to maintain a balance between the number of free and slave states?

Maintaining a balance between slave and free states would preserve the South's political power in the Senate.

2. Comparing Describe the different views expressed by Lincoln and Douglas in their debates regarding slavery and racial equality.

Lincoln argued that slavery was wrong and that African Americans were entitled to all the natural rights described in the Declaration of Independence. He also said that the nation could not endure "half slave and half free." Douglas argued that trying to end slavery would lead to war between the North and the South, and that African Americans were not the equals of whites.

WRITING ABOUT HISTORY

Creating Imagine that you are a northerner who is opposed to the Fugitive Slave Act. Create a poster that demonstrates your views to display in your town.

Students might mention that the Fugitive Slave Act is immoral, that it forces antislavery states and communities to help slaveholders by returning fugitive slaves, and that it encourages the kidnapping of free African Americans by bounty hunters.

Chapter Tutorial
The Civil War

IDENTIFYING TERMS Choose the term or name that correctly matches each definition.

_____ 1. strategy used by South to try to gain foreign support

_____ 2. general in charge of the Confederate Army in Virginia

_____ 3. most important Union general in the western war

_____ 4. constitutional protection against unlawful imprisonment

_____ 5. general who led Union forces in the Battle of Gettysburg

a. Robert E. Lee

b. *habeas corpus*

c. George C. Meade

d. Ulysses S. Grant

e. cotton diplomacy

UNDERSTANDING MAIN IDEAS

1. What advantages did the South have at the beginning of the war?

_____

_____

2. How did the outcome of the First Battle of Bull Run challenge northerners' assumptions about the war?

_____

_____

3. Why did the Union want to gain control of the Mississippi River?

_____

_____

4. How did Lincoln try to silence northerners' criticisms of the Civil War?

_____

_____

5. What was Sherman's total war strategy?

_____

_____

Chapter 19 Tutorial, continued

REVIEWING THEMES

1. Science, Technology & Society Describe the ironclads and how the South used them.

_____

_____

2. Economics How did the Civil War affect the economy of the South?

_____

_____

3. Citizenship In what ways did African Americans contribute to the war?

_____

_____

_____

THINKING CRITICALLY

1. Drawing Conclusions Why do you think northern leaders considered the capture of Richmond to be so important?

_____

_____

2. Identifying Cause and Effect How do you think Sherman's March to the Sea affected the residents of Georgia?

_____

_____

WRITING ABOUT HISTORY

Describing Imagine that you fought alongside General Thomas J. Jackson in the First Battle of Bull Run. In a journal entry, record the details of the battle and its importance to Jackson's career.

_____

_____

_____

_____

IDENTIFYING TERMS Choose the term or name that correctly matches each definition.

_e (p. 584)_ **1.** strategy used by South to try to gain foreign support

_a (p. 587)_ **2.** general in charge of the Confederate Army in Virginia

_d (p. 590)_ **3.** most important Union general in the western war

_b (pp. 597-98)_ **4.** constitutional protection against unlawful imprisonment

_c (p. 601)_ **5.** general who led Union forces in the Battle of Gettysburg

a. Robert E. Lee

b. _habeas corpus_

c. George C. Meade

d. Ulysses S. Grant

e. cotton diplomacy

UNDERSTANDING MAIN IDEAS

1. What advantages did the South have at the beginning of the war?

The South had many skilled military leaders and was fighting on its home soil.

2. How did the outcome of the First Battle of Bull Run challenge northerners' assumptions about the war?

Many northerners assumed that the war would be quick and easy. Their crushing defeat at the First Battle of Bull Run showed that the war would be very difficult.

3. Why did the Union want to gain control of the Mississippi River?

Union leaders wanted to capture the Mississippi River to divide the states of the Confederacy, damage its trade, and launch attacks on the South's transportation network.

4. How did Lincoln try to silence northerners' criticisms of the Civil War?

Lincoln suspended the right of habeas corpus, _the constitutional protection against unlawful imprisonment, and had many critics of the government arrested and thrown in jail._

5. What was Sherman's total war strategy?

Sherman wanted to destroy the South's economy and its willingness to wage war by attacking civilian as well as military targets.

REVIEWING THEMES

1. Science, Technology & Society Describe the ironclads and how the South used them.

Ironclads were armor-plated steamships introduced during the Civil War. The South converted a captured Union ship into the ironclad Virginia and used it to sink a number of U.S. Navy ships before it was driven off by the Union ironclad Monitor.

2. Economics How did the Civil War affect the economy of the South?

The Civil War did tremendous damage to the South's economy by destroying many plantations, railroads, cities, factories, and by freeing the slaves that the southern economy depended upon for much of its labor.

3. Citizenship In what ways did African Americans contribute to the war?

Thousands of African Americans served as Union soldiers, escaped from southern plantations (which damaged the southern economy), and performed labor for military units.

THINKING CRITICALLY

1. Drawing Conclusions Why do you think northern leaders considered the capture of Richmond to be so important?

By capturing the capital of the Confederacy, Union leaders hoped to destroy the Confederate government and break the will of the South to continue fighting.

2. Identifying Cause and Effect How do you think Sherman's March to the Sea affected the residents of Georgia?

Students should mention that the destruction caused by Sherman's troops shocked and angered many Georgians. Students might also note that African Americans in the South might have viewed Sherman's march more positively.

WRITING ABOUT HISTORY

Describing Imagine that you fought alongside General Thomas J. Jackson in the First Battle of Bull Run. In a journal entry, record the details of the battle and its importance to Jackson's career.

Students should note that after the Union troops pushed the Confederates back, Jackson's soldiers held firm and led a counterattack that crushed the Union forces and sent them fleeing back to Washington. They might mention that the Confederates could have done even more if they had not been tired and confused. Students should also describe the chaos of the battlefield.

CHAPTER **20**

Chapter Tutorial

Reconstruction

IDENTIFYING TERMS Choose the term or name that correctly matches each definition.

_____ **1.** process of reuniting the nation

_____ **2.** laws that greatly limited the freedom of African Americans

_____ **3.** Northern-born Republicans

_____ **4.** special fee required before an individual could vote

_____ **5.** system of trading labor for the right to farm land

a. poll tax

b. Black Codes

c. sharecropping

d. Reconstruction

e. carpetbagger

UNDERSTANDING MAIN IDEAS

1. How did the Freedman's Bureau help newly freed slaves and other poor people?

_____

_____

2. What was Johnson's Reconstruction plan?

_____

_____

3. Why did southern states adopt Black Codes?

_____

_____

4. How did African Americans participate in Reconstruction?

_____

_____

REVIEWING THEMES

1. Constitutional Heritage How did the Thirteenth, Fourteenth, and Fifteenth Amendments provide greater rights to a larger group of Americans?

_____

_____

2. Government What did southern governments accomplish during Reconstruction?

_____

_____

3. Culture In what ways did African Americans exercise their rights as freedpeople?

_____

_____

THINKING CRITICALLY

1. Comparing and Contrasting How did conditions for white southerners differ from those for freedpeople immediately after the Civil War?

_____

_____

2. Analyzing Information Explain how the sharecropping system created new hardships for many farmers.

_____

_____

WRITING ABOUT HISTORY

Persuading Imagine that you are an advisor to President Johnson. Prepare a speech that will persuade him to require the southern states to outlaw Black Codes.

_____

_____

_____

_____

IDENTIFYING TERMS Choose the term or name that correctly matches each definition.

_d (p. 621)_ **1.** process of reuniting the nation

_b (p. 627)_ **2.** laws that greatly limited the freedom of African Americans

_e (p. 633)_ **3.** Northern-born Republicans who moved to the South after the Civil War

_a (p. 637)_ **4.** special fee required before an individual could vote

_c (p. 639)_ **5.** system of trading labor for the right to farm land

a. poll tax

b. Black Codes

c. sharecropping

d. Reconstruction

e. carpetbagger

UNDERSTANDING MAIN IDEAS

1. How did the Freedman's Bureau help newly freed slaves and other poor people?

The Freedmen's Bureau helped newly freed slaves by distributing food, providing legal assistance, and establishing schools.

2. What was Johnson's Reconstruction plan?

Johnson's plan gave amnesty to all southerners who pledged an oath of loyalty and promised to support the abolition of slavery. His plan also said that wealthy southerners and former Confederate officials had to receive a presidential pardon to get amnesty. State governments had to be re-established by those who had taken the loyalty oaths. These new state governments had to declare secession illegal and refuse to pay Confederate debts.

3. Why did southern states adopt Black Codes?

Southern states hoped the Black Codes would help white southerners economically by forcing African Americans to work for them and re-creating the conditions of slavery.

4. How did African Americans participate in Reconstruction?

African Americans were strong supporters of the Republican Party and its Reconstruction policy. They participated by voting and by being elected to office. They also tried to enforce African Americans' civil rights.

REVIEWING THEMES

1. **Constitutional Heritage** How did the Thirteenth, Fourteenth, and Fifteenth Amendments provide greater rights to a larger group of Americans?

These three amendments expanded the rights guaranteed in the Constitution to African American men, people born in the United States (except American Indians), and naturalized citizens.

2. **Government** What did southern governments accomplish during Reconstruction?

Reconstruction governments funded schools and public institutions, prohibited racial discrimination, and built or repaired bridges, public buildings, and railroads.

3. **Culture** In what ways did African Americans exercise their rights as freedpeople?

African Americans exercised their freedom by getting married, traveling, taking new last names, and buying land to farm for themselves.

THINKING CRITICALLY

1. **Comparing and Contrasting** How did conditions for white southerners differ from those for freedpeople immediately after the Civil War?

Although both groups faced hardships because of the destruction of the land and shortages of food, white southerners had often gone into debt to support the war and were still considered enemies by the Union. Freedpeople, on the other hand, had some support from the North and they had the hope they felt after gaining their freedom.

2. **Analyzing Information** Explain how the sharecropping system created new hardships for many farmers.

The sharecropping system encouraged farmers to buy things on credit, thus perpetuating a cycle of debt. In addition, the sharecropping system put pressure on those sharecropping to grow cotton, eventually creating a glut of cotton that led to lower prices for cotton and lower profits.

WRITING ABOUT HISTORY

Persuading Imagine that you are an advisor to President Johnson. Prepare a speech that will persuade him to require the southern states to outlaw Black Codes.

Students should explain to Johnson that Black Codes attempted to return African Americans to slavery-like conditions and that ending these conditions had been one of the purposes of the war. They might also appeal to Johnson on the basis of justice, explaining that in a country like the United States, which supported liberty and freedom, such laws would be out of place.

Name _____ Class _____ Date _____

IDENTIFYING TERMS Choose the term or name that correctly matches each definition.

_____ **1.** areas of federal land set aside for American Indians

_____ **2.** religious movement begun by Wovoka

_____ **3.** large deposit of precious ore

_____ **4.** lean and tough mixed breed of cattle

_____ **5.** farmer on the Plains

a. Ghost Dance

b. bonanza

c. reservations

d. Texas longhorn

e. sodbuster

UNDERSTANDING MAIN IDEAS

1. What caused the conflict that led to the Battle of the Little Bighorn?

_____

_____

2. What difficulties did western miners face?

_____

_____

3. What led to range wars?

_____

_____

4. How did the Homestead Act enable more people to move West?

_____

_____

REVIEWING THEMES

1. Economics How did federal policies encourage companies to build railroads?

_____

_____

2. Culture What types of people moved to the West, and what were their motivations for moving there?

_____

_____

3. Geography How did farmers adapt to the conditions on the Great Plains?

_____

_____

THINKING CRITICALLY

1. Drawing Inferences How did living on reservations affect the ability of American Indians to practice their traditional ways of life?

_____

_____

2. Identifying Cause and Effect How did the impact of cattle on the natural environment contribute to the decline of the Cattle Kingdom?

_____

_____

WRITING ABOUT HISTORY

Explaining Imagine that you are a leader of a Plains Indian group. Write a letter to the commander of the U.S. army, letting him know why your people do not want to move onto a reservation.

_____

_____

_____

_____

IDENTIFYING TERMS Choose the term or name that correctly matches each definition.

c (p. 650) **1.** areas of federal land set aside for American Indians

a (p. 652) **2.** religious movement begun by Wovoka

b (p. 655) **3.** large deposit of precious ore

d (p. 660) **4.** lean and tough mixed breed of cattle

e (p. 668) **5.** farmer on the Plains

a. Ghost Dance

b. bonanza

c. reservations

d. Texas longhorn

e. sodbuster

UNDERSTANDING MAIN IDEAS

1. What caused the conflict that led to the Battle of the Little Bighorn?

Gold was found in the Black Hills where the Sioux had reservation land. The U.S. government insisted that the American Indians sell their lands. The Sioux resented these demands and began fighting with the U.S. Army.

2. What difficulties did western miners face?

Miners faced a number of dangers while mining, such as the dangerous methods they used to mine, poisonous gases, and cave-ins. In addition, nonwhite miners were often discriminated against.

3. What led to range wars?

Range wars were the result of competition for land among large ranchers, small ranchers, and farmers. As barbed wire allowed ranchers to fence off large tracts of land at low cost, some farmers and smaller ranchers began to fight back by cutting the wires and moving onto the land or by stealing cattle.

4. How did the Homestead Act enable more people to move West?

The Homestead Act allowed people to buy land at a reasonable cost and enabled people to move West by providing them a place to live and a way to make a living.

REVIEWING THEMES

1. Economics How did federal policies encourage companies to build railroads?

The government helped companies build railroads by providing them with loans and large land grants, which the companies could sell off to pay for construction.

2. Culture What types of people moved to the West, and what were their motivations for moving there?

People moved into the West from everywhere in the United States and many foreign countries. They came from a number of different ethnic groups, including African American, Chinese, Mexican and Mexican American, Norwegian, Swedish, Danish, German, Czech, and Russian Mennonites. All of these migrants were motivated by hope for a better life.

3. Geography How did farmers adapt to the conditions on the Great Plains?

Farmers on the Great Plains developed new kinds of farming equipment and techniques to deal with the challenges of the Great Plains. For example, to cut through the tough sod, they used John Deere's deep steel plow. They dealt with the lack of water by practicing dry-farming methods.

THINKING CRITICALLY

1. Drawing Inferences How did living on reservations affect the ability of American Indians to practice their traditional ways of life?

Many American Indians often lived by hunting buffalo, which provided them with food, clothing, and shelter. When they were limited to hunting and farming on reservation lands, they could not hunt and had to find new ways of living.

2. Identifying Cause and Effect How did the impact of cattle on the natural environment contribute to the decline of the Cattle Kingdom?

Because the cattle had overgrazed the land, when two unusually cold winters hit, the cattle were left without food to eat and many of the herds starved, ruining the ranchers.

WRITING ABOUT HISTORY

Explaining Imagine that you are a leader of a Plains Indian group. Write a letter to the commander of the U.S. army, letting him know why your people do not want to move onto a reservation.

Letters should explain the Plains Indians' traditional ways of life and how these ways were destroyed by confinement on the reservations. They might also discuss the quality of the lands that they might be sent to and the corruption of Bureau of Indian Affairs agents. Finally, they might address the issue of fairness and justice, explaining that the Plains Indians had been there first and had lived on the land for their whole lives.

EPILOGUE

IDENTIFYING TERMS Choose the term or name that correctly matches each definition.

_____ **1.** elected president in 1988

_____ **2.** killing of six million Jews by the Nazis

_____ **3.** co-founded Hull House in Chicago

_____ **4.** plan for dealing with the Great Depression

_____ **5.** made most forms of discrimination illegal

a. Jane Addams

b. George Bush

c. the New Deal

d. the Holocaust

e. Civil Rights Act of 1964

UNDERSTANDING MAIN IDEAS

1. Discuss the difficulties farmers faced in the late 1800s

_____

_____

2. What contributions did African Americans make to America culture in the 1920s?

_____

_____

3. How did women and African Americans contribute to the World War II war effort?

_____

_____

4. How were Martin Luther King Jr. and Malcolm X similar? How were they different?

_____

_____

5. What were some of the successes and failures of the Clinton administration?

_____

_____

Epilogue Tutorial, continued

REVIEWING THEMES

1. Global Relations Why did the United States enter the fighting in World War I?

_____

_____

2. Citizenship What were some significant events of the civil rights movement?

_____

_____

3. Economics What did NAFTA allow?

_____

_____

THINKING CRITICALLY

1. Evaluating Could prohibition have succeeded, or was its failure inevitable? Explain your answer.

_____

_____

2. Supporting a Point of View Do you think the United States should have fought in the Korean War?

_____

_____

WRITING ABOUT HISTORY

Explaining Imagine that you are one of President Kennedy's advisers during the autumn of 1962. You have just seen photographs of Soviet nuclear missiles being installed in Cuba. Write a memo to President Kennedy outlining three possible courses of action, including a naval quarantine. Be sure to discuss the strengths and weaknesses of each approach.

_____

_____

_____

_____

IDENTIFYING TERMS Choose the term or name that correctly matches each definition.

b (p. 708) **1.** elected president in 1988

d (p. 698) **2.** killing of six million Jews by the Nazis

a (p. 686) **3.** co-founded Hull House in Chicago

c (p. 694) **4.** plan for dealing with the Great Depression

e (p. 704) **5.** made most forms of discrimination illegal

a. Jane Addams

b. George Bush

c. the New Deal

d. the Holocaust

e. Civil Rights Act of 1964

UNDERSTANDING MAIN IDEAS

1. Discuss the difficulties farmers faced in the late 1800s

To feed the growing population, many farmers borrowed money to buy land and new machinery. However, the combination of more farms and greater productivity led to overproduction and lower crop prices.

2. What contributions did African Americans make to America culture in the 1920s?

African American composers and musicians developed jazz and authors and poets contributed writings in the Harlem Renaissance.

3. How did women and African Americans contribute to the World War II war effort?

Both African Americans and women signed up for service in World War II, and millions of women and hundreds of thousands of African Americans also went to work in factories to help produce materials for the war effort.

4. How were Martin Luther King Jr. and Malcolm X similar? How were they different?

Both Martin Luther King Jr. and Malcolm X were religious men. King believed in integration whereas Malcolm X promoted racial separation.

5. Why did the United States and the countries of Western Europe create the North Atlantic Treaty Organization (NATO)?

NATO was formed to provide mutual defense against military threats.

REVIEWING THEMES

1. Global Relations Why did the United States enter the fighting in World War I?

The United States entered World War I because Germany attacked U.S. merchant ships.

2. Citizenship What were some significant events of the civil rights movement?

Brown *v.* Board of Education, *integration of Central High School, Montgomery bus boycott, Freedom Rides, March on Washington, Civil Rights Act of 1964, Voting Rights Act of 1965, the assassination of Martin Luther King Jr.*

3. Economics What did NAFTA allow?

NAFTA allowed goods and services to move freely between Canada, Mexico, and the United States.

THINKING CRITICALLY

1. Evaluating Could prohibition have succeeded, or was its failure inevitable? Explain your answer.

Most students will probably argued that its failure was inevitable since the government could not watch people all the time.

2. Supporting a Point of View Do you think the United States should have fought in the Korean War?

Answers will vary, but some students might argue yes, the United States had a responsibility to stop the spread of communism. Other students may argue that the United States should not interfere in the affairs of other countries.

WRITING ABOUT HISTORY

Explaining Imagine that you are one of President Kennedy's advisers during the autumn of 1962. You have just seen photographs of Soviet nuclear missiles being installed in Cuba. Write a memo to President Kennedy outlining three possible courses of action, including a naval quarantine. Be sure to discuss the strengths and weaknesses of each approach.

Memos may suggest a variety of approaches, including, no action at all, an economic embargo, a naval quarantine, protest at the United Nations, or military action. The potential dangers and benefits of each course of action should be considered.